The Grief Practice

in memory of _____

Note To Readers:

This book is intended to be a resource and support for grief and is not a replacement for psychological, psychiatric, or medical care.

Nothing in this book is prescriptive or intended to provide medical or psychiatric advice. Please consult your mental health care provider, physical therapist, or regular health care provider with concerns or questions.

Please consult with your doctor before trying any of the yoga shapes or practices.

The Grief Practice

stories of surviving loss
practices for supporting loss

Monique Minahan

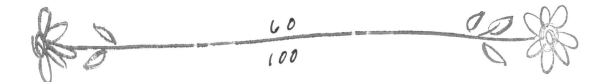

This is the story of grief, as told by you.

created in honor of Nathan Vance Oligny

who introduced me to grief

Table of Contents

Part I: STORIES

Part II: PRACTICES

STORIES

PART I

Our stories of grief begin long before we lose.

They begin with the ways we were raised, loved, accepted or rejected.

They begin with the ways we were taught to be proper and sane and the things we were taught to sweep under the rug.

They begin with the silence in our homes and in our hearts about everything that ever mattered but was never spoken.

They begin with the people who listened or turned a deaf ear to our early heartbreaks... the ones that taught our heart what it can expect from the world.

They begin with the shame that was planted just under our skin.
The kind that keeps us from trying or speaking, reaching in or reaching out.

They begin with love. The unconditional, incomparable, unsurpassable kind that we were gifted as children or find as adults.

They begin with us. Our stories of us shape our stories of grief.

And although they are stories of how things ended,
they are also stories of how we begin.

Again, from here, with the hearts on our sleeves and the truth in our throats.

This is the story of grief.

I

I hold his hand as he awaits radiation treatment
He is anxious and sad and scared
        ("me too," I yell silently)
My mom, his wife, will be there when he returns

"Can you stay with him?" asks the well-meaning nurse
My two-month-old son also waits for me, while I sit
Two men—one young, one dying—need me
I think of this moment often

II

I think of those mysteries within us
That shimmy and shake
Reverberating in our bones and muscles
Then leaving us, reluctantly,
Through eyes or skin or mouth

And sometimes those exit booths are ports of entry
Sneaky, subtle borders
Allowing outside shocks to settle in
Our bones and muscles
Amplifying those mysteries

III

An enigmatic man
Gregarious and full of life
And yet harsh and fearful
In his absence I feel those reverberations
That have settled deep in my body
It's hard to tell sometimes which mysteries are my own,
which are his

So I take comfort in those shimmy shakes
They are what make me whole
Echoes of generations
—past or passing or to come—
All treading on unsettled ground
or fault lines
or
or

-Joely Pritzker

She birthed my soul and broke my heart. I stood at the foot of the bed of a woman who was told only a few months prior that she was cancer free. I stood at the foot of the bed of a woman who was beginning a new chapter that wasn't the chapter she wrote. I stood at the foot of the bed of a woman who could never let go of anything. I stood at the foot of the bed of a woman who never taught her daughter anything different.

In silence, I heard a wisdom I didn't want to hear, asking me to perform a task untaught to me. Any and all audible words fell down my throat and were swallowed whole. But time kept moving. Days began to fold and my swollen eyes were the only guardians keeping me afloat. She was dying and at a pace separate from my ability to digest its truth. Cancer is a ruthless and deviant prey. Even when you slaughter it, it can regenerate and return so quickly no one has time to react. Or at least that was the beast that lay inside my mother.

It was all unfolding without my permission, without my consent, and without my input. In an attempt to breathe reason into my lungs I remember sitting in the hospital courtyard with my aunt trying hard to feed myself, a task so difficult when your body is riddled with shock. Blindsided is an unfair fight that left my body a blender of emotions.

As I looked around in numbness, I noticed a cardinal bird sitting on the chain-link fence behind us, looking at me. I watched him cock his head from side to side and then he took off. When he landed on the chair next to me, I came to attention. With no words spoken, my aunt and I exchanged our mutual surprise. He kept staring at me. Looking at my plate, I had little left to offer and said out loud I was sorry to him, as if I was a terrible host. He jumped on the table, hopped next to my plate and continued to cock his head side to side. A few seconds later he flew away. And although that behavior may be commonplace for a sparrow or a black bird, I knew it wasn't for a cardinal. I was blindsided again, but this time I could feel magic that carried no logical words with its story.

I had returned to the waiting room inside the hospital where I shared my experience with my family. However I couldn't find the words to explain what I felt versus what I saw. My sister looked at me as if in shock. She had just returned from home to bring my mother's books so we could read to her as she lay in her hospital bed. She brought back "The Gift of the Red Bird." A book about a divine encounter, a book about letting go. On the cover was a beautiful red cardinal. The magic that carried no words offered itself up in its first clue.

From there I found myself slowly uncovering the horrific beauty of the space I was in. The Divine was whispering through this trauma. My family and I soon found ourselves in a room full of doctors and the time had come. The room was stuffy, their charts were oppressive, and the walls were void of inspiration. The army of white coats surrendered their fight and were nudging us to make the deal final, to remove all life-sustaining support from her. In a dead tone the words simply fell out of my mouth and tumbled onto the table. I don't know what to say. My head and my heart haven't had this conversation yet.

I think this is the space where grief lies, this desert road between the heart and mind. A battlefield.

As the war began, my heart made a fantastic case of why it should win and my mind rebutted with facts that could crush her, and did. But something was born for me that day; a channel, a space, a conduit. This death was leaving a seed. Within the piles and piles of grief, the whisper of the Divine was becoming louder and louder, making its presence known.

She died. Without my heart's permission. Shouldn't I be older when this happens? How does one go forth unmothered?

A few months before she died we had a monumental conversation in the driveway where I confessed I saw my marriage to be no different than the broken one she felt she was in . She looked at me from the passenger seat and said, "Run, Terri." I suddenly felt the weight of the seatbelt across my chest. My thoughts traveled faster than time offered. The lineage to my pain was mirrored, tied and sewn.

Our exchange became the affirmation that allowed me to finally have the guts to hit rock bottom, a moment I needed to surrender to it all. Grief became the center, the holy ground of the ultimate pivot. It inspired me to pack up my things and move to another state to rebuild my life. Leaving behind my marriage and all things known, I began the long process of draining tequila from my veins and everything else that no longer served me.

Grief and death had an intimate way of showing me how to be alive.

Grief made me unsettled, uncomfortable, and questioning everything. My relationship with grief seems never-ending as it leaves and comes back, even years later, just to show me another layer of myself I must remove. Oh, the grandeur that lies within it.

I think grief has a mission that cannot be described with any word found in the dictionary. Grief will have its way with you with or without your permission, so I chose to be the road less traveled and surrender to it. It was a hard and lonely road. Grief, for me, became the Divine teacher teaching the class on the art of letting go.

Maybe I am more mothered than I think.

She birthed my soul and broke my heart. But as they say, when things are broken that is how the light gets in. For me, grief was an intersection where the Divine collided with this human experience of mine. And even though my heart was gutted into a million pieces, the whisper showed me how and why it is possible to survive its demise.

We are definitely not as alone on this journey as we think and feel we are.

-Terri Hug

His infinity girl-
Is what he says I am,
Flattered, touched,
And then wondering and wandering,
Where does that leave You?
My love in heaven.
How can there be room for two in infinity?
Deep talk is what this must be-
No answers.
Answers for days.
Swimming in the mystery,
I can't seem to find a way.

There's only space for You-
Even though you're memories and energy.
Still, I feel loyal to you.
You're dead. But you're dead.

And this man who is here,
He says I am his infinity girl-
Can I still be yours too?
Can that be?
Because I love you still,
I always will.

I know some days there's just space for You.
And after a while I can return to what's alive and holding my hand.

I remember when it used to be so easy to say forever.
But infinity feels like forever,
And my heart will always love you,
I can say forever with You,
Can I say it for two?
Is there space for two?

But forever is forever changed,
And You have been my forever,
And now I am his forever.

Destiny and infinity,
As deep and wide as my eyes can't see-
There must be room for two,
If my heart can love you too.
You can be my forever too.

-Alexandria Romero

I lost my daughter, Alexandra, when I was five months pregnant.

Twenty-one weeks to be exact. A routine ultrasound at nineteen weeks revealed some abnormalities in her brain and other parts of her body. The various doctors we consulted with all told us the same thing. No matter how we phrased our questions, their answers all came to the same conclusion.

In an act of deep love, we chose to end her life in a warm, familiar, loving environment, in my womb. Our journey of saying goodbye began just over one month ago.

I have never known grief like this before.

I've heard stories of people losing their children and always thought that would be one of the worst pains in life. It scared me, and now here I am, sitting in my new reality. Some days it just sits in the background of my busy life as a wife and mother of a beautiful, boisterous, and active toddler.

Most days my grief shows up in a more impressionable way.

Sometimes it comes as a beautiful lightness, and that's when I know that her spirit is with me. It's when I know that, even though she is gone, she is within me, running through my blood, and she will *always* be there. This brings me so much joy.

Her passing is a reminder to love more, to smile more, to take in all the little moments because they are what make life remarkable. In these moments my laughter feels uplifting. My son's little face and smile and my husband's kindness and humor remind me of all the gifts I am blessed with in life.

Sometimes, though, my grief is a true and unbearable sadness. Usually my sadness builds in a series of small circumstances and then just gushes out in a really big mess.

For example, a couple days ago I met a beautiful couple at the playground. They had two children and were expecting another. The mother was due just one month before I would be. A month ago we could have swapped pregnant mama stories, but now it just brings a quiet reminder of what's gone. My mind drifted away from her and from my son, who I was pushing on the swing, back to Alex and a lost world.

Today my hairdresser messaged me to remind me that I needed to come in for a cut. She asked me about the baby. Not wanting to text about my situation, I just ignored it. And then I caught up with a friend for the first time since losing Alex, Of course I wanted to talk to her, but in the craziness of breakfast and life, I didn't want to bring up the emotions. So I'm not surprised that today I am crying and overwhelmed and in a dark place. I know it will pass.

But this is my new world. Back and forth between light and dark. I know this will not end. I'm not expecting it to. There will be many more encounters, more triggers. I just hope my response will soften.

I don't want to forget her, so I'm okay with it.

But it's a very new loss. I hope with time I will find more tools to deal so when the unbearable sadness comes, it doesn't knock me out for the day.

—Rachel Zatulovsky

On October 18, 2003, I returned to Phoenix from teaching a yoga workshop and was greeted at the Sky Harbor airport by my father and two brothers with the news that my 20-year-old-son, Brandon, and his 19-year-old girlfriend, Lisa, had been shot to death while camping overnight. They were sleeping in the back of her mother's pickup truck in BumbleBee Arizona, about an hour north of Phoenix, AZ in celebration of their one-year anniversary.

When they didn't show up for work on Saturday morning, we all knew something must be wrong, but they weren't discovered until Sunday. There was no robbery, no apparent motivation, and although it was broadcast to the country on CNN and America's Most Wanted, the case was never solved.

I am very fortunate that I have another child, Jessica, my beautiful daughter. This was a devastating loss for all of us. An unthinkable tragedy. An unimaginable pain. My deepest sadness and fear at the time of this tragedy was that I would never again know joy.

I feared that my life would always have a tone of sorrow. I set out on a mission to work in the direction of reclaiming my joy and reason for living. My spiritual journey had officially begun and after almost two years, and thousands of frequent flyer miles, landing into the open hearts of friends and strangers, I realized my son's death could renew my own life and purpose.

I have been practicing yoga since 1987. I was certified in Iyengar yoga in 1994 and in Anusara Yoga in 1999. Since that time I have been traveling full time, teaching yoga workshops and retreats all over the world. I believe it has been the steadfastness and inner strength I have learned directly from my yoga practice that has enabled me not only to survive, but thrive. For the first two years, I was in so much emotional pain that I couldn't help but share it in my workshops. I shared my grief openly with my students and many of them thanked me for being an example of someone not afraid to be real and true to her feelings.

I travel full time teaching yoga and believe it is a healing mission for me to go out and share what I have learned about regaining joy after such tremendous loss.

I would like to let more people know that there is a way to mentally, emotionally AND physically transform the pain and suffering of the past and truly regain motivation and a sense of peace. My healing process was also assisted by a terrific counselor and the teachings of Abraham-Hicks' principles of the law of attraction. After all these years, it has become clear to me that the union of the human experience with the knowledge of the Divine presence within has helped me to embody the feeling of joy and freedom that it seemed this tragedy had taken away.

The power of Yoga is immense and priceless. I am grateful.

-Desirée Rumbaugh

My mother was tragically killed in an automobile accident when I was 23 years old.

I had a toddler. My mother made sure I had a birthday cake each year. My 23rd cake was my last.

I was numb for a year. I couldn't function. My heart felt like it was ripped out of my chest. I knew that it had changed me.

Our culture makes loss and death so awkward. No one tried to reach out to me, other than telling me to go to work and go on with life.

Over the years I've suffered a great deal of pain. In the past couple of years I have finally started moving forward.

It took yoga, god, sometimes unconventional things.

I got my mother's name tattooed on my wrist. Whatever a blessing is on earth, it is the same in heaven. That opened up the healing process for me. It was acceptance. It is also a proud badge of honor that I wear. I have no other tattoos. It gives space for others to start the conversation of the name "Linda Sue," as well as a back story, but more so the positives.

It gives me the opportunity to celebrate my mother and her legacy. I am her legacy. Her advertisement. It is okay to embrace it daily.

-Judy Smith

There was a baby, but no heartbeat. I was in for my standard 8-week appointment, and from the measurements it looked like the baby had stopped growing at 6 weeks, 1 day. I was then diagnosed with a missed-miscarriage. Basically, your body hasn't figured out the fetus has died and carries on like you're still pregnant.

Tears filled my eyes and I couldn't believe the news we were just given. In that moment, the gravity of our situation was crushing. She continued the sonogram and started telling me about my "options" while she finished up. She left the room, and I just looked at Jon.

On the way to the doctor's office I had asked Jonathan, "What if there's something wrong?"

He shook his head and whispered to me, "How did you know?" Now, looking back on that, I cannot think of anything other than a mother's intuition. How could I have possibly known? Since then, I have trusted my gut feeling more often than not. I just wish that I had been wrong on that particular occasion.

1 in 4 pregnancies ends in miscarriage. To me, miscarriage is like this dirty little word that no one wants to mention. We don't want to think about it if it hasn't happened to us. But the truth of the matter is that it's real, and it's something that will affect many, many mothers... a friend, a sister, an aunt, maybe even your own mother.

I left that office with the worst possible news. I was still pregnant and carrying around a baby, but that baby was no longer living. I couldn't help thinking that my body had failed me. I felt like less of a woman. I couldn't do the one thing that I was intended to do as a woman: procreate and successfully carry a child for 9 months. My body hadn't figured out what it needed to do, and I felt like I had failed.

The miscarriage was a deep, dark secret we carefully buried in our marriage. I'm sure it was hard for Jonathan, but it absolutely wrecked me and tore me apart from the inside out. It felt like there was now a small, baby-sized hole growing steadily larger in my heart that could be filled by nothing. The grief was horrible, and something I felt no one could understand. I had never before struggled with depression, but I now know how hard and horrible that darkness is.

I felt like the loss of that child would swallow me up into a pit of despair. And, if I'm honest, it did. It's hard to admit, especially in the midst of the situation, but I needed help. I sought that out in a family counselor who helped me immensely.

After my D&C surgery, I came out of anesthesia and the first sound I heard was that of a crying baby. Not the best sound to wake up to when you've just had a surgery to remove your own deceased child. I didn't know it at the time, but the hospital, Mary Birch, was going through some remodeling. So, unfortunately, those mothers recovering from a D&C were in the same room as the mothers recovering from a C-section. Not great planning on the hospital's part, but maybe it couldn't have been avoided.

And when I was discharged, I was given paperwork about the procedure and about my specific physical recovery. However, I was given no paperwork on my mental recovery. As I explained earlier, I desperately needed it.

Months went by before I felt strong enough to speak with a family friend about the situation. Cheri Kuptz, what a blessing she was, suggested a couple of things to me after listening to my story. First, she thought it would be good for me to write the hospital a letter to explain my situation. After a lot of prayer and reflection, I finally sat down, wrote a letter, and sent it off to Mary Birch.

I was completely shocked when a nurse called me and spent 45 minutes walking me through each and every single one of the points I had made and was deeply moved that I had even bothered to write my experience down, much less send it their way.

She explained to me that the recovery room was a temporary solve, and that she knew how hard and traumatic that must be for patients to wake up to that situation; but that they did already have plans to separate out those recovery rooms specifically for that purpose.

We also talked about the discharge policy for D&C patients. She said it was up to the patient's recovery nurse to determine whether or not that patient received paperwork regarding grief counseling and their mental recovery.

I mentioned that not all people may show signs of their grief immediately upon waking from anesthesia. In my case, specifically, the grief didn't hit me until a week or so later. Not to mention I'm probably also too proud to let a stranger know when I'm having a hard time. She thought I made a good point and said she would talk to her supervisor about issuing the brochures to every D&C patient. Again, I didn't think much of this.

You can imagine my surprise when I received a package in the mail a couple of weeks later with a letter letting me know her supervisor had approved her request! She also sent over the papers and brochures each patient would receive after their discharge, so I could see them myself.

After months of depression and grief, I finally felt like there was a silver lining from this whole experience. If my miscarriage was able to help just one mother like me who was suffering the same fate, then I felt like there was purpose behind my situation. I'll never know why that baby didn't survive, but I choose to believe that God had a plan. And as corny as it may sound, maybe the loss of my child was for the sole purpose of helping other women to not experience a soul-crushing grief for as long as I did. At least that is what I will hope for.

After all of this, Cheri Kuptz also recommend I design something around my miscarriage experience. We came up with an idea for greeting cards to gift to those specifically struggling with miscarriage.

I deeply believe that the moment you decide you want to have children is the day you actually become a mom. Just because you don't have a physical child in front of you, and even because you may have lost your baby to miscarriage, doesn't make you any less of a mother. And don't let anyone make you think otherwise! We need to get rid of the notion that you have to have a physical child to be a mother. There are so many of us hoping, willing, praying, and wishing for a child. And I think that, in and of itself, defines the very start of motherhood.

From this idea has come my first line of greeting cards: *The Miscarried Mom Collection* of our Noble Greetings, specifically designed for those women struggling with miscarriage, infertility, pregnancy-related issues, and those trying to navigate the difficult journey to baby.

After much prayer, design, and procrastination, I finally launched them into the world in June of 2016. I'd like to think they are one-of-a-kind, as I haven't seen anything like them available, and I am just so proud to finally be sharing these with the world.

During my process of creating these cards, and walking through this grief journey myself, I always felt like there was something pulling at me to keep going - to keep moving and to help others. I don't have the best words to explain it myself, so I'll finish with a quote I found that sums up how I felt during that point in my life: "God often uses our deepest pain as the launching pad of our greatest calling."

-Katelyn Woolley

I knew he was gone before I got the phone call.

I felt it.

Ron had left Seattle two days earlier to go back East. For the first time in his adult life his parents were back together and the four of them - Ron, his twin brother, and his mom and dad - were going on a cruise.

I was in midterms. I had been accepted to naturopathic medical school. Ron and I had recently packed up our little Manhattan apartment and embarked on our cross country journey to Seattle. I was terrified and unsure of myself as a medical student. Ron had the confidence in me that I lacked in myself; he was my rock. He made sure I ate well and cleaned tirelessly so as to lift whatever extraneous burdens from my already over stressed mind and body. When all else failed, he made me laugh. Ron's mind worked unlike any other person I've ever met. He saw the world differently and because of that gift, found humor in things one wouldn't ordinarily find humor in. He was weird and I love every strange bit of his being.

I spent the evening studying, trying to push the fact that I hadn't heard from him in hours out of my mind. Evening turned into night and I tried my best to sleep so I'd be rested for my physiology exam the next morning.

It didn't work.

At 4:00 a.m. I made a distressed phone call to my parents in New York. I told them I knew something was wrong. They tried to soothe me. My mom even assured me saying, "Ron is all right. He's a survivor." And he was a survivor... just not this time.

His brother found him in the morning when he went to ask him what kind of donut he wanted for breakfast. Ron had gone to sleep the night before and didn't wake up.

The cause of death is unknown, at least to me. I've had to make peace with that - a torturous and ongoing process. I've come up with a thousand hypotheses. Sleep apnea? Accidental overdose? Heart failure? Blood clot? Allergic reaction? Flu?

In the end it doesn't matter. My Ronnie is gone.

The life I had worked so hard to create crumbled around me. I left Seattle hours after I found out he was gone and I never went back.

I gave up and I gave in.

I let myself be held and carried by those beside me through the darkest days of my life.

A few months after Ron's death a friend invited me to go to India with her. I wasn't ready, but then again I wasn't ready for Ron to die either. No one is fully prepared for what life gives you. I went on the trip.

I traveled and bombarded myself with new sights, sounds, smells, and experiences. I learned to love food again. I submersed myself in so much stimulation I had little space to feel grief, instead dealt with snippets of pain when they bubbled to the surface.

After a month of traveling Asia, I landed in California. I set up shop in Oakland where I was greeted with open arms. I proceeded to tear down every bit of the remaining shreds of the life I had cultivated with him; it was too painful to let it stand.

I was sad but also angry at Ron for leaving me here, alone. I imagine myself standing on an empty stage set with a sledgehammer. I smashed in the foundation and ripped down the curtains. I stomped it to the ground until my old life was barely recognizable. Advisable? I don't know.

The thing about death and grief is that there is no instruction manual. There's no guide. Starting from scratch was the only thing I could think to do. I began a new life, with new people, in a new city, with the only traces of Ron being those in my heart.

Eventually, I reapplied to school and transferred to a campus in Southern California.

I would have never in a million years imagined myself living in San Diego, but I do now. Perpetual sunshine and just a short walk to the ocean. I walk on the beach daily, usually in the evenings. I call it sunset therapy.

I find comfort in knowing the sun will set and rise every day. It's reliable. It won't leave me.

The ocean is loud. The surf crashes and no one can hear me crying, if crying is what feels right that evening. The ocean is big and the sky is bigger. It gives me the expansive space I need when so often during the day it feels like I must contain my grief, keep things down, "hold it together." The cyclic nature of the tides reminds me that I'm still here, we're still here. Life keeps living. I keep breathing.

"Everything happens for a reason," they say.

Fuck that.

"Everything happens" is where that sentiment should end.

Maybe there's a higher power, a "greater plan," but that doesn't soothe a heart that's been ripped to pieces.

Everything happens. And when it does, you may crumble.

With a certain trust in oneself, you can rise again - a new version. Maybe even a softer version. Human beings are remarkable like that. Our bodies, our minds - they are capable of so much. Capable of loving and hurting deeply, simultaneously.

-Kaylyn Gatto

It's been a year since my Dad died... since his second and final death, the permanent one.

He died the first time in 2012. It was a Friday. He was 63 and had an aortic dissection, aortic aneurysm and two strokes. "The worst they'd ever seen," reported the medical professionals of the dissection that split and tore his aortic wall the furthest it can go from his neck to his groin.

If you save this man's life, it'll be your greatest moment" stated one of the approximately 40 assistants to my Dad's heart surgeon as his aorta burst while he was under surgery for the dissection.

During this most difficult, risky and delicate medical procedure, he suffered two strokes as a result of being without oxygen to his brain for eight minutes and flatlined... clinically dead. They only gave him a 25% chance of surviving the seven-hour surgery and stated that even if he made it through, he would be "brain dead for life."

I was 28 years old and recently fulfilled a deep desire to live on my own. I had just moved into an apartment right on the beach in San Diego and was embarking on a personal spiritual journey. I had begun pursuing my dream of having my own business and was having success getting this going alongside of a work-at-home job that I absolutely loved. I was dating the man I was sure I was going to marry and was grateful for life itself.

My Dad was a protector, a helper, a supporter, a caregiver, a provider, a leader, and a guide. He was dependable and reliable. No matter what the situation was, I knew I could reach out to him and he would literally be there for me, stopping whatever he was doing to help out in any way he could.

I was independent, but realize now that my Dad personified safety and security to me. He was a constant in my life and I never doubted if he cared about me. He regularly checked in or found a way to let me know he was thinking of me. Just touching base," as he would say, or with a note in the mail attached to a $20 bill encouraging me to keep working hard, but "remember to have fun." He cared for me not just physically, but about my happiness too.

The first irreversible seismic shift in myself and my reality.

I remember arriving to the hospital in Pennsylvania and seeing my Dad hooked up to machines, with a breathing apparatus, a trachea, and various tubes and lines going in and out of him... completely comatose. It was him, but it wasn't him. My first thought was, That's my Dad's face and his hands and his hair and his body, but that's not my Dad.

Obviously I hoped for the best, but while trying to get some sleep one night at my parents' house in my old bedroom, I remember thinking about everything that was happening and the very real possibility that he might never wake up. It was then that the most horrific animalistic sound came out of my body... a screaming cry, a yelp, a howl. It was unlike anything I had ever heard or felt and it overtook me, coming up from my guts and out of my mouth.

It was grief.

No matter what was to be, the Dad I had, my "Original Dad," already died.

I visited him every day at each place. He went from being in a coma for two months in the ICU to Progressive Care to a step-down unit/skilled nursing facility to finally qualifying for rehabilitation and being released to go home on Valentine's Day 2013, where he would continue with various in- and outpatient therapies.

He miraculously survived and recovered. But he, myself, and life were never the same.

I didn't entirely know what that meant, but I know an unconditional love for my Dad had emerged on that fateful Friday. It's an otherworldly, soul mate, best-friend connection that defied the "typical" father/daughter relationship dynamic we previously had. I got to know a "new" Dad...Dad 2.0.

We connected and shared and laughed together. In the almost five "extra" years with him, his health, happiness, and quality of life became my priority and focus. I cared for him daily in one way or another, both in person and at a distance in Pennsylvania and California. The love was so real and powerful that it superseded everything else. He was worth it.

Even with the previous experience in 2012 and other strange forms of grieving my living, breathing Dad at different points, I still never could have imagined or prepared for losing him again, permanently, with his second and final death, just 4 years and 9 months later.

He died. My Dad was dead.

Finding out was like crashing into a solid brick wall at full force... shock, disbelief, and confusion. I couldn't and sometimes still can't process it. I just kept repeating myself and crying uncontrollably. It's surreal and bizarre and elusive, while simultaneously being the harshest, most stark reality.

My grief was immediate and automatic. It was debilitating and I was incapacitated. I could hardly move and barely ate or slept until that was all I wanted to do. Grief has affected every part of my being and area of life... my brain, my body, relationships, work, finances, beliefs, interests, etc. It's been an incredibly isolating, lonely, and solitary journey.

For me, the death of my Dad was annihilation. My soul was severed... something broke and separated, not just a part of me, but all of me... a whole self. Who I was died with my Dad on September 20th, 2017. A cosmic hole ripped above me and the earth below me cracked apart.

I can't explain the connection between my Dad and me, but I know that losing him has been like losing the very air that I breathe; like trying to breathe without lungs. I remember wailing and choking so hard that it felt as though my soul was trying to get out of my body; like my insides were literally coming out or trying to, but couldn't. It felt like dying while still alive.

Somehow, I am still alive. Sometimes I'd rather not be and sometimes I can't believe that I am. Sometimes the pure pain is so visceral and vile that it consumes me and sometimes I'm despondent and apathetic. Sometimes I know what a gift and miracle it is to be alive and sometimes it's a living hell, like a nightmare that never ends. Sometimes it's a dark abyss and I wonder if I'm going insane and sometimes I'm so acutely aware of how short and fast life actually is and am grateful for it again. Sometimes I smile and sometimes I cry. Sometimes I have genuine laughter and moments of joy, even if only in remembering my Dad.

His life and death are his. The grief is mine.

He's not just his death. He's not my grief. I can endure my grief, which will be with me in some way, shape, or form for the rest of my life. But it's this very same precious life without my special Dad that seems unbearable.

Sometimes I can't breathe and sometimes that's all I can do.

-Robyn S.

There is a problem with Baby B's brain, they said.

It looks like severe ventriculomegaly. This will mean a very, very difficult life for this baby, if she even survives.

This is when my experience of grief began.

The first loss was the loss of hope for two healthy babies, all that I had been hoping for. *Just let them be healthy and normal and arrive safely.*

Guilt.

Is it ok that I am pining for the other baby to be ok?
Is this happening because I was initially fearful and dreading a twin pregnancy?

Guilt.

Will we at least get one healthy baby to take home and love?
How can I even think this?
I feel so selfish.
How could I be happy bringing one baby home and watching the other die?
How can I continue living with one of my children gone, forever?
Will I be able to laugh again or enjoy anything?
Will this baby suffer?
What if they are wrong?

Panic.

My first experience of grief was my very first panic attack. I could hear my husband talking to me, but I just kept rubbing my legs, sobbing, rocking in the rocking chair in our living room. The sobs were coming from a place I didn't know existed. They radiated out of my body into the room. It felt like my chest and guts were knotted and trying to straighten themselves. I paced. The beautiful sunny day was supposed to bring happy news. We should be out celebrating our babies. I couldn't sit still or lay down. I felt like my body and mind was doing so much work to process what I knew was going to be the death of at least one of my children.

The days went by.

I tried not to crumple into a heaving mess of human mass every second of every hour of the next 9 weeks and 4 days.

People watched me, they saw me. They knew what was happening. Some tried to help, some didn't, some ignored me.

I couldn't be helped in this time period. I so much appreciated that people knew about what was happening and were genuinely sad and wanting to help me, but I didn't want it. I felt like I was making everyone sad with my terrible news and that I should stop bringing everyone down, perk up, be happy that at least one baby is healthy.

Be happy? Get right out of my face with your "be happy that one baby is healthy."

So angry and withdrawn, so tired of creating awkwardness everywhere I go. Nobody knows what to say, what to do.

Some are trying because they love me, and I feel that love. And it is helping me on some level of which I'm not aware of at this point.

I am angrily resentful of the meaningless problems people are complaining about, that I used to complain about.

I am ashamed to say I withdrew from my sick little girl, on my left side, helpless. On future scans I wanted to see my little boy first, to immediately know he was ok. Knowing she was not ok became normal somehow. The worst normal.

I felt her move very infrequently. I quietly comforted her and myself late at night, rubbing the left side of my body where she lived. I hoped that she could feel that she was loved and wanted and that I would do everything possible to ensure she didn't suffer a minute of her life.

This became my goal for her. I wouldn't see her have any medical interventions to disrupt her tiny existence for however long it lasted.

I had so many worries about her. Would she be in pain? Would she be hungry? Would she struggle to breathe? Was I a terrible person for not letting the people do all of the things to "save" her?

I work in a children's hospital. I have seen children who never smile, eat, see, hear, or breathe on their own. I did not want this for her or for our family.

More guilt, more self-doubt.

The day came. My water broke at 29 weeks. I held on in the hospital for 4 days.

My little girl, Baby B, held on long enough so that her brother, Baby A, could get the medication he needed to survive being born so early.

He was born first, screaming, and bigger than he should be. They brought his little face close to mine for an instant. The best instant of my life.

She was born. The room was very quiet. She didn't cry, she didn't look like a normal baby, but she was beautiful. I held her little body and touched her head. I felt her make a few very small movements on my chest. I smelled her. I tried to make my body remember every second, to somehow store this into a special spot in my brain, so I could recall it perfectly to keep her with me forever.

They wrapped her in a blanket. She started to feel cold and looked dusky. I held onto her, my husband held onto her, I held onto her again.

The journey of loss and grief thus far had been mostly worry and uncertainty, but the moment they took her away was the moment the sob turned into something more primal, a force I couldn't control or understand.

I sat in that room and watched them take my dead daughter away, forever. I'd never know what her cry sounded like, what color her eyes would have been. Her life was gone from us, forever, gone, ended.

This memory, of the nurse carrying my little girl, Alice, away is the most excruciating thing I endure in life when I recall it. I am so thankful to have memories of her, but this one has not gotten softer.

It rips my soul apart.

I am thankful she did not suffer in her short life; that she was with us and loved her whole life. In the darkest of time, I try to focus on the love we have for her, that she got to experience every second she had on this earth.

To continue to love someone so much who is gone is a lonely path.

I wonder if I think about her too much or too little.
Should I be doing more to honor her?

I have a little box of pictures of her and her tiny purple hat. I take them out sometimes and let the feel and smell of her into my body. The sadness is so overwhelming sometimes that I can't catch my breath, like there is so much grief inside of me that it can't escape in tears, so it comes out in small pieces and I keep holding onto it.

I will hold on to it forever. I took that box of her things out to be with her often after they were born.

It has been over two years and I haven't taken it out for awhile. I feel guilty about this. As her mother, I should visit with her more. I should bring flowers to the beach where we scattered her ashes more.

There is no straightforward set of rules of how often you should honor your dead child.

It feels a little less raw two years later. My favorite thing is when people mention her name and remind me that they remember she existed.

This doesn't make me sad. It makes me feel less alone in my grief.

My mother has made a point of mentioning Alice often. She includes her in mother's-day crafts and on their birthday. I know she thinks about her often, and she has been a great support.

I feel guilty that others have grieved Alice and I did not comfort them. I have a friend, Katie, who I met through the multiple birth organization in my province. She, too, lost one of her twins, Caroline, at birth. I feel I can tell her anything that I am feeling at anytime. She truly gets it.

This total understanding, acceptance, and unwavering support has been invaluable in turning my grief into a manageable pile of mess most days.

When others share their stories it somehow normalizes the heartbreak and daily practice of living life without someone you love.

Sometimes I am blindsided by twins out in the community or little girls who would be around her age had she survived. Depending on the day, sometimes I can smile and remember her fondly, and sometimes it fills me full of such a rage-filled sadness that my entire day is left in shambles.

There are not too many people in my life who understand how the sight of a double stroller can ruin an entire day. I think most people would think that was ridiculous and that I am overreacting.

I have few safe spaces to talk about these complicated feelings of sadness, guilt, and rage. Most of all, I'm not sure how they would be received by most people.

More awkwardness. They would feel like they needed to say something to make me feel better, but there really isn't a puzzle to be solved.

It just needs to come out and be received and understood as best as possible.

-Molly Blackie

My 21-year-old brother unexpectedly died. And then my relationship of over seven years unexpectedly ended. My life as I knew it fell apart, not once, but twice in the span of three short months.

Previously, if I heard a story similar to mine, I would have responded with, "I could never do that. I would fall apart." Now I am part of a club that no one wants to be in.

I have found that grief and loss are exactly as bad and somehow worse than I thought they would be.

When things went from unthinkably bad to traumatizingly worse, my friends and family came through for me in the biggest and most meaningful ways. They reminded me how to love myself.

By gracefully showing up for me, going above and beyond what was asked and selflessly caring for me when I needed it the most, they taught me the true meaning of motherhood.

In the weeks following my brother's death, many of my aunts and cousins came to stay with my family. They did things like the laundry, grocery shopping, and played interference to the parade of well-meaning visitors.

But, they did more than menial tasks. To encourage us to stay active, they invited us to go on walks with them each day. To nourish our bodies, they made smoothies in the afternoons and chocolate chip cookies at night. Every morning they greeted us with hugs and loving smiles. They showed me, through their kindness, what it looks like to give to those truly in need. They physically and emotionally mothered me and my family through some of the toughest days we faced.

Friends texted me throughout the weeks, sending messages as simple as, "Thinking of you." They sent funny articles and YouTube videos, in case I felt like being distracted with a laugh. They asked how I was doing and actually wanted to know the answer.

After the break-up, my circle of friends rallied together, more focused than ever. When I didn't know what I was feeling, let alone how to explain what I needed from them, they gave me the time to figure it out. They gave me space to simply be how I was, to show up without pretense or fear if I was good enough. They answered the late-night phone calls that began with me gasping for breath through sobs. They texted me before I woke up with, "I love you and I'm here for you" messages.

One friend, already a mother to a young daughter, invited me to stay in her guest room with little to no notice needed. She gave me a safe place to sleep so that I didn't have to make the 90-minute drive twice in one day. But, more importantly, she let me take over her living room weekly with my tears. She listened as I asked different versions of the same questions over and over again. How could this all be happening? Why? Now what?

Slowly, our visits became happy reunions and our relationship began to resemble a 50/50 split in caretaking. Sure, sometimes it is still 60/40 or even 80/20, but I'll never forget the few months in early 2017 when she let me take up 100% and loved me exactly as I needed to be loved.

My brave friends, who had been through similar experiences of loss, listened, and shared that they had been in the place I was now. They understood that it felt hopeless and like I would never get back to myself. With their help, I learned that I needed to give myself grace and time to move through this. They repeated that it probably won't feel "all better," but that I will get better at dealing with and managing the feelings associated with all this loss.

Knowing that there was hope that I would not always feel this way allowed me the ability to remain mindful and take things one day at a time. I began to learn and slowly accept that I was doing all the emotional work I could, and that healing of this magnitude was going to take time.

At one point or another, nearly everyone said a version of the same very powerful words, "I am so proud of you." "I am proud of you for driving yourself to therapy." "I am proud of you for speaking at the service." "I am proud of you for keeping grace and kindness as priorities." "I am proud of you for doing your best."

When someone communicated these emotions, it sparked something inside of me. I thought, If all these women whom I admire are proud of me, then I must be onto something. I must be doing something right. Soon I started recognizing the things I was proud of myself for, too.

For weeks I operated in the strangest state of in-between. Not wallowing and yet not fully living. Going through the motions. I slept a lot and was also never quite awake. For the second time in three months, my world split down the middle and swallowed me whole. Everything seemed to be ending and yet my body kept on living.

I nurtured myself by continuing to take care of me. Each night I poured myself a glass of water and took my vitamins, supplements, and medications. I said a silent prayer of gratitude towards my body. Every morning I got out of bed, showered, and ate something. Some mornings I got right back into bed and would instantly fall asleep.

A key for me became continuing ahead. Not moving on, but rather, moving forward.

My mom and sister resisted the urge to jump in and do things for me, perhaps because they saw how helpful it was for me to take care of myself. That act was life-affirming and, in many ways, was the start of me building up my new foundation, picking up the pieces of the broken one, filled with smashed dreams, shoulds, what-ifs, and could-have-beens. This new one is being built of sturdy stones that have been scarred by what I've experienced and lost. The pieces are rough but the worn edges fit together easier now. There's not so much resistance. Like a puzzle where the pieces were being forced together before, now they slide into place.

One Sunday afternoon a friend texted that she wanted me to call her. Selfishly, I figured it was to check on me. But when I called, she let me know that she was pregnant. My heart immediately broke open for the new life that was starting during what felt like the darkest period in mine. I couldn't imagine the many emotions she was feeling, just like she couldn't fully understand the pain I was going through. And yet, here we were, on the phone, crying for each other and for both of our new beginnings.

To the women who give of themselves, mother me, and continue to stand as my witnesses while I begin the process of growing into this new version of me: Thank You.

-Andrea L'Heureux

At first my grief was surprisingly shocking in a physical way.

I felt tingly inside, and when I cried I felt it strong in my belly - like it felt when I was falling in love with Mike. I can't remember much about the first three weeks after he left except that horrible, wonderful feeling in my belly when I cried.

It was shocking that Mike was gone, even though we knew it was coming. His rare neurological disorder, Progressive Supranuclear Palsy, had been diagnosed twenty-two months earlier. In addition, we had been experiencing the effects of his unacknowledged disease for two years prior to diagnosis.

We lived full-steam-ahead for nearly four years and then BAM! Life as I knew it was forever changed. No wonder I was in shock. Never mind the loss of my love and life partner. That was bad enough. But the physical and emotional energy needed for caregiving left me no time to think about what would happen after Mike left. I didn't have a clue it would hit me so hard. I'm a "strong person" according to many who told me so during Mike's illness. I didn't realize it exactly this way at the time, but now I know I was in shock for at least the first three weeks.

Our living arrangements are unusual in that before we even were aware Mike was sick we sold our house and embarked on our empty-nester dream. An open-ended, full-time motorhome living and traveling adventure. We spent time at the Oregon coast, Southern California, and the Sierras in Northern California as volunteer camp hosts about 7 months of the year and traveled randomly the rest of the time.

Once we got the diagnosis we decided, after much discussion, to stay the course. Now we were scheduled as usual (for this time of year) to be camp hosts in a state park campground less than one month after Mike left.

I knew if I kept our routine for the both of us I would be following the sage advice "don't be making any major changes during the first year." I would also be at the perfect place to move from initial shock to the knee-buckling grief stage.

The next four months were unbelievable. I was at the beach in San Diego and lived my camp-host life "almost normal" except for two things.

I allowed myself to relax. I took many things off my to do list, spent a lot of time knitting (I had put this activity on the back burner during Mike's illness and now I found it very therapeutic) and focused on healthy eating, exercise, and sleep.

I interrupted my "almost normal" time on a regular basis to express and embrace my grief over what just happened to Mike, to us a couple, and to me as an individual.

There was this slow and unbelievable realization that my life as I previously knew it had been stolen. There was incredibly painful grief because I liked my life and my partner. We were in it for the long haul and having a good time. How could this be happening? There were many healing tears.

I did not try to hold back the tears because crying felt good – an admission that I was injured in a physical way.

I began a private journal almost immediately upon leaving the town where Mike departed when I was finally alone and could begin to grieve in private. I wrote about my memories of what just happened and of our life together, about my feelings of love for Mike, and expressed pain for his and our loss.

Each time I had a beach walk and a good cry, I wrote what was on my heart and mind and sent this to friends and relatives via their preferred communication method.

Being connected to others made me feel good.

My next move, during months six and seven, was to travel alone to Yucatan Peninsula, Mexico. Mike and I had been there twice before, same time of year. Now I made it my mission to retrace our steps and blog publicly about my experience of traveling alone and how I felt about the fact he was not here in person this time.

I know Mike was with me on this trip because of the feeling I got deep in my belly numerous times when I would retrace our steps to a town, attraction, or even a restaurant where we had been previously. Love and spontaneous tears always made me feel good.

One night I went to a restaurant where I knew I would hear live music. The band was a guitarist and a percussionist who were seated on a loft above the outdoor patio seating area where I was given a table. They finished up the song they were playing when I entered, and the guitarist spoke in Spanish to the crowd for a minute before starting the next song, which was the ONLY song they played in English the whole time I was there.

They covered the song by Bob Dylan (one of Mike's favorite artists) "Knock, Knock, Knockin' on Heaven's Door." I'm crying right now just thinking about it. Coincidence? I think not. I enjoyed an uninvited take-my-breath-away cry of joy at being connected and told Mike "I love you, too."

Mike always told me "There will be one constant in our lives... you and me." I always believed him, and now my actions will prove him right. He will live forever in my life, heart, and mind. I will continue to cry when it feels good to do so, and right now I don't want that feeling to go away.

—Denise Tomczak

47

I was at work when I found out Jen died. I had just spoken to her on the phone two days prior. Upon finding out, I didn't yet know how she died, but I had a feeling she killed herself. She had attempted once before, and this time I was worried that she actually "did it."

Jen and I met at work and immediately became BFFs. Although we met in our twenties, our friendship felt very lighthearted and pure, like two girls swinging together on a swing set.

Jen was one of the most thoughtful and caring people I had ever met. She always gave great advice and did things to help me lift my spirits. She would make funny faces or dance around to make me laugh. When she laughed, she would hold her belly and laugh this silent laugh, and her whole face would light up.

What I would give to see her laugh again.

Two days after she died, our circle of friends learned that Jen had jumped off a tall building. She had left notes for her family. I had last seen her in person just eight days prior, and she had given me a card that she made during her last psychiatric hospital stay. It read, "Thank you for being a true and wonderful friend and walking with me through this crisis." At the time, I didn't think it was going to be the last card I would receive from her.

I barely remember the first month after she died. I was a total zombie. I couldn't go back to my own apartment for three weeks. I stayed with my parents, who didn't know how to handle my emotions, but tried their best. A few of my friends were very supportive and were grieving their loss of Jen at the same time.

During the first year-and-a-half after Jen died, I did every type of grief work I could; psychotherapy, hypnotherapy, a support group, a workshop, chakra healing, you-name-it. I was on antidepressants for one year. I also learned to cut loose a bit more, which I really needed to do. I made it to the beach at least once a week. I also traveled, domestically and out of the country. It was good to be away.

It has been almost nine years since Jen died. She has been gone more than twice as long as our friendship lasted, and I still miss her every day.

As painful as losing her was, my grieving process has led me to realize how short life can be and to go after what I really want. I learned not to worry about trivial things.

I moved to the city I have always wanted to live in. I make time for the people who bring positive energy, and I cut ties with those who are toxic. I still love deeply, now doing so with the awareness that it will always come to an end.

**The card
JEN
gave me.**

- Miriam Siyam

It's been about 10 days since I said my last goodbye to you.

I hope you don't mind this being a little late, but I wanted to give you some time to settle in in Heaven and read the letter I sent with you. You know I'm fibbing, don't you? You always could see straight through me. I admit it, I cry every day for you and miss you so much it's been hard to write it down.

Do you know? On the day I said my final goodbye to you, my legs were wobbling so much I didn't think I'd even be able to walk through the Chapel to see you. But I did (as you know.)

Joel, you looked so handsome it took my breath away. You had on your new basketball jersey that we bought you and your favorite white throw that you took to bed every night tucked around you. I sprayed it with my perfume, as I know you always loved me to do that. You looked so peaceful. Your lovely red hair was perfect. I just wanted to see your beautiful blue eyes, but you were too fast asleep for me to see them. I'll never forget them though.

Laying there, you reminded me of when I woke you up on Christmas mornings to tell you Santa had been. You were never in your bed. You'd always be sleeping in whatever 'pop up tent' you had at the time, on the floor. The year I remember most was when you had your Thomas the Train tent. Do you remember? I woke you up and saw your beautiful smile and then nearly got knocked over as you ran into the living room. Kyle was still a baby then, but I bet he was looking and thinking, "What's my brother all excited for?"

I held your hand and kissed your cheek. I hope you weren't embarrassed, because only you and I were there. I put my left hand on my heart and my right hand over your heart and sang "You are my sunshine" to you. I know the words came out a little wobbly, but I was never the best singer, as you know. I sang that song to you when you were still in my tummy. I sang it to you when you were a toddler to help you sleep. Many years later it became your Granddad's song to you. I hope he's still singing it to you now that you're with him in Heaven.

Joel, did you see the amount of people that came to say 'goodbye' to you too? Over 200 people! So many people whose lives you touched and, of course, all of us that loved you to pieces (and still do.) The love in the room was overwhelming. I hope you now see what a wonderful young man you were (are.)

Now here's the personal bit. (I can hear you saying, "Oh, no, knew this was coming....")

There is not a minute of every day that I don't think of you. I know you're in a much happier place now, but it doesn't stop my tears. I hope you understand. Half of my heart died when you left me. It will never re-grow. Kyle and I will carry on as best we can, and I'm hoping someday there will be more smiles than sadness. You would have wanted that. I hope they have a basketball court up there so everyone can see how good you are. Maybe they have Rubik's cubes so you can challenge Granddad. (I know who'd win though!) When you get time, can you make me another origami swan, please? You can give it to me when I see you again. That would be lovely.

So I will write again soon, but never forget how much we love you. Please come down from time to time in my dreams to let me know what a great time you're having. I'd love that. You ARE and always WILL be my
sunshine, and I love you more than I can put into
words.

All my love, now and forever, Mom.

-Kerrie Ragsdale

My grief hurt, and so I drank. I spent the first three months after his death on his recliner in the fetal position and I drank. I drank a lot. It masked the pain, marginally.

Three years later, I don't drink so much anymore, and I still feel the grief bottoming out in me. The pit in my stomach, as I write, feels as if a bowling ball rests in there. Tears flow freely. They just come. I can be standing out in public and, without warning, they come. I was always a shy person, but this grief I don't hide. I don't feel embarrassed, like I need to "cover it up" or "put on a brave face" because this pain is real, and there are others that KNOW this pain. I know I am not alone.

He died on June 15, 2014, early Sunday morning. I had been asking him all week about going to a festival with me in Chicago. He had been 'iffy' about it. I was ready to go Saturday morning and I teased him, "Well, are you coming or not coming?" He reached for an old work shirt and put it on. With that, I said to him, "Well, I guess you're not coming." I told him I had to get going so I wouldn't miss my train. I gave him a hug and a kiss and said, "I wish you were coming with me!" Then I left.

It was the last time I saw him alive.

I traveled to the city on my own many times, so it was per usual. I thought about how hard he had worked that week. Lots of overtime, not easy for a guy of 52 years who had Type 1 diabetes for 30+ years (a lot of the time it was not well-controlled). And I could tell he was tired. I worried about him and thought it was probably better that he stayed home and took it easy. The city was always so much walking, which he probably didn't need to be doing.

I attended the festival and did some shopping. I got to the train station, just missing the 6 o'clock train, so I had to wait for the later train. When I arrived home, I saw him sleeping and snoring in our bed. I got ready for bed. On my way to sleep, I touched his shoulder to let him know that I had made it home okay. He didn't wake up. He was in a coma and snoring.

In a second my world came crashing down all around me in a whirl of EMTs and emergency room and his family. He died from a severe hypoglycemic reaction Sunday morning. He was gone, and the suddenness of it sent me into shock and searing pain. He died on Father's Day, leaving his two children fatherless and me a widow.

I think sometimes that I should wear a black veil so that maybe the non-grievers might be a little more understanding, because grief is not always so visible and it manifests itself differently in every individual. Many people, including friends, don't realize that. A veil might be a gentle reminder as to why I'm not acting 'normal' to them.

I thank God for my fellow widows and widowers. We hold each other up when the weight of our storms hit, and these storms are monsters. They are the friends who still help me through this miserable, haunting grief.

It feels like I have a flaming hot poker stabbing me in the heart. I feel abandoned, not just by him, but also by some of my closest friends and confidants. THIS HURTS. I realize that they (the "friends") don't understand the depth of this pain and won't until they are in it themselves.

I think about him daily. I talk to him and I can hear his voice in my head. He tells me he loves me. He tells me he's so sorry. He tells me he never meant for me to go through so much pain and trouble. He's sorry that I was left with a mess. And that completely describes it. A mess. A mess that is in my mind, my daily living; a mess that can never be cleaned up. This intangible mess of emotions. This mess of losing my partner, my home, and my life as I knew it. My world fell out from under me and went on a downward spiral. A big mess. The tears flow.

I would love to see the day when people don't leave you when you are grieving. When they come out of their comfort zones and cushy homes and acknowledge the grieving person. I don't mean two weeks after the death, I mean two years after! Call it what you want. A disorder? Depression? Complicated grief?

No. I simply loved him with my whole heart, and I lost him. You can't sugar-coat it, because grief is raw, ugly, and messy. What helps is contact from others. Just come over and sit with me. Call and tell me you were thinking about me and listen without interrupting when I talk about my lost love. Don't judge. I want to keep his memory alive, I'm not trying to make you sad. I am grasping the memory of him as tightly as I can, and I'm NOT letting it go! This is very healing for me.

Crying is good. Venting is good. Friends who care are good. I write about this grief because I loved a man. I loved him with the abandon of a wide-eyed, love-struck, 16-year-old girl. We met in high school, and he used to flirt with me relentlessly as we stood at our lockers. At the 30-year high school reunion we were reunited and started dating. We fell head-over-heels in love. He asked me to marry him twice. I said yes on May 7, 2011, eight months after we reunited.

He always used to say that he "would find me anywhere." He did. And to this day, he still does. Maybe all this hearing voices stuff makes people think that I am crazy. No, not crazy. Enlightened. My grieving experience has put me in a realm where I can sense what I never have before. Ask any widow or widower and they will tell you about their heightened awareness (and it's all drug-free!)

I remember him so strong and handsome, with a wink and that devilish grin of his. I miss him. I miss just sitting with him, being in his presence. Watching the goldfinch and hummingbirds as we had our morning coffee on the patio. We didn't even need to talk, just being there was enough. Sure, we had our bad moments like any other couple, but we always worked it out.

Grief has a way of giving you tunnel vision at times, only seeing the good of the person you lost. But I see it all. I cry for him and I curse at him. That is normal, I'm told. I will always love him.

I miss you so much, Hotstuff, and thanks for the hummingbirds.

These pages are damp with my tears. Just like his shirts that I still wear. Grief is the price you pay for love someone said, and that is the honest truth. My grief for John is the hardest thing I've ever faced. In my heart, I know I will be facing this grief the rest of my life, but the love, the love will remain. The constant in my life remains a big mess.

A big mess of love mixed with pain and humility, this grief of mine.

-Deborah Berthiaume

Tightness across my chest, heaviness and numbness in my arms and lips. I want to cry, but won't. Today the feeling seems endless and overwhelming.

Today I grieve for my sister.

I am... was the youngest of 4 daughters. There are only two of us left. In November, after three years of living with ovarian cancer, the tumor became so large that it strangled and obstructed her bowel, making it impossible for her to keep any food down. She starved to death.

But my grief is complicated, layered, and weighty because:

It is June 21st today, the longest day of the year.

Today I grieve for my husband.

28 years ago my first husband died suddenly from a massive cardiac event. He was alone in his hotel room whilst he was on a business trip to London. I remember him like I saw him yesterday and I think of him with love.

By the time he died. we knew that our two-year-old son was severely disabled with cerebral palsy.

Usually when I tell people about him, I explain that he is patient and kind and makes the absolute most of his life despite being quadriplegic, with altered speech. I am a fiercely devoted, loving mother to all my three sons, but recently I have started to have flashes of him driving, running, working, having children... talking to his two younger brothers about their girlfriends.

Recently I have started to long for all that is dead for him.

I remarried in 1993, and in 1997 our wonderful second son was born.

He was diagnosed with Asperger's syndrome when he was 11 and Type 1 diabetes when he was 15.

Usually I say how lucky he is to be born with such wonderful intelligence. He gets straight A's in his chosen subject; he is studying at a top university and has a girlfriend and a few friends.

Today I am grieving all that he has lost.

He never picks up on social cues. So much goes on that he does not notice, and people reject and get angry with him because of that. He will never have that wonderful, exquisite connection that I enjoy with my few close friends. My heart is broken for him.

I lost a baby son. He was called Sean. I don't want to talk about that today.

I had coffee with my friend yesterday, and she said to me: "You are so inspiring. I always feel better when I have spent time with you."

I know I have that effect on people. I have travelled the grief path and can help and hold them.
But recently I have withdraw... recently my enormous capacity to empathize with others has worn thin.

You see, I experienced another death when I was really young.

I will try to explain by telling you about this image imprinted into my mind:

A series of coffins in the order in which they died ... my eldest sister... my father... my husband... my baby son Sean... my mother... my next sister...

But in amongst these coffins is another. A small, almost ethereal child's coffin. In it lies a little girl who is around two years old. She has enormous blue eyes and brown curly hair. She was so full of life before she ended up in there.

My father abused me, and that is how I see what happened to me.

A therapist once said to me, "So you are surrounded by death."

Am I? Am I surrounded by death? I don't think so.
I am laden with grief.
I am changed by my grief and I am surrounded by life.

You see, I survived because I built a garden.

57

It started with the unruly clematis that was growing outside our house. One day I went out and untangled it. First I pruned the excess branches, then I dug posts into the ground and tied strong green wire between them. I gently tied up the stems that needed support. I dug some plant food into the ground at its roots, and that spring I was rewarded with a profusion of pink flowers.

With a kind of comfort that I had never experienced before, I moved into the rest of my unkempt plot and started to experiment with digging and mulching and hoeing and vegetables and bedding and huge, lush, herbaceous borders.

I have a sign, which is more or less permanently on my front door:

IN THE GARDEN

My garden saves my life.

Sure, in winter there is die-back and the ground is cold and frozen. But I know that it will thaw and I know what treasures always lie underground.

In fact, my wellington boots, secateurs, and gloves are waiting for me, and I am going to go outside right now!

—Anonymous

A few days after my sister died, I left the laundry in a dryer at my old apartment complex's laundry room for a several days. I couldn't bring myself to go get it. Why bother? Nothing mattered. I was tired. When I finally got around to going down (mostly because I was out of clean towels), I found my linens neatly folded. This never happens. I expected my items to be untidily balled up on the counter. Maybe my downstairs neighbor had heard what happened by that point. Maybe something led a stranger to provide the care I needed then. It felt significant.

It's been over a year since my younger sister, Ashley, died

The first 48 hours were hell. My phone would not stop buzzing. It was not until much later that I would appreciate each attempt at condolences, no matter how imperfect. The acknowledgment of our loss mattered.

Some days (most days) I am "fine." I go to work, I go to class, everything flows smoothly. I do touristy things with visitors. I take selfies with the Statue of Liberty. I am fine.

Other days, I pick a fight with my (perfect) partner for not being supportive enough or in the ways I want right then. I feel guilty. I apologize. I sob uncontrollably and my head throbs. I can't make it to class. I need my couch and the softest blanket and Grey's Anatomy for six hours. And that's fine.

There are dates that highlight the hurt, draw the pain near to the surface and encourage me to act out and/or isolate. Holidays, birthdays, anniversaries, the obvious ones. Some aren't neatly marked on the calendar. You can't plan for them all.

Other people move on. It's not wrong. It's just the way things work for most of us. I am not the friend that remembers every significant date in my network's life. Without social media, I wouldn't remember to send you a photo of a dog in a party. We do our best, and I try to remember this.

Today, October 2nd, 2017, would've been my sister's 26th birthday had we not lost her in August of 2016. Last night, October 1st, 2017, a gunman opened fire on a country-music-going crowd in Las Vegas. At the time of this writing, there are 58 confirmed deaths.

That's 58 families with a new death date to dread.
58 families who will struggle through early October for the rest of their lives.
58 families who will cry at each holiday gathering this year.
58 families who may not make it into work on their lost loved ones' birthdays.

I am angry today. I am angry about senseless violence, about the state of our country, about all of the unnecessary pain those families will face from this day forward.

But I am most angry about the nature of grief. I am angry that I feel guilty for craving more support today.

Everyone has something to say about grief.

It gets better with time.
Sending thoughts and prayers to the family.
Stay strong.

But the truest tidbit I've heard is the significance of the support offered once a little time has passed. Once everyone else has moved on. Once it feels silly to keep asking for what we need.

Don't stop checking in on your friends and family that have lost someone. Don't be afraid to "bring it up." Bring them up. Talk about the loved ones we have lost. Share a memory. Acknowledge our pain. Hold us while we cry and bring us our favorite foods. It will be appreciated more than you are capable of comprehending, until it's offered to you when you feel alone and forgotten. When you're envious of the urgency of a national tragedy.

Show up and fold the laundry. Even after a year has passed.

-Allison S.

My life was touched, opened and forever changed by a little 4-year-old girl
named Zoe.

Her name means "life," and I believe that is why she came here; to teach us what it truly means to live. To live from the heart space, rooted in love, deeply connected to compassion, joy, wonder, and one another.

Zoe is the only daughter of my best friend Angela and her husband Kevin, I am her "Aunty" and my husband John her "Uncle." I was there the moment she was born and also the moment she left this earthly plane. John and I were unable to have children for some reason. I understand now that is likely because we were meant to have this experience of being parents through loving Zoe.

In every way she felt like a daughter to me - we had and still have a very special connection.

Zoe was one of my favourite people to hang out with. It was magical to be with her. I was "home" in her presence - you could not be with her without smiling or laughing. She was beautiful, bright, she loved to sing and dance and help with whatever you were doing. She enjoyed the finer things in life - macaroons, pear/gorgonzola pizza and dark chocolate, while also scaling rocks at her cabin, jumping wildly on the trampoline in a tutu and working in the garden. She was fearless and fancy - the greatest gift in my life and in the lives of many others.

One of Zoe's best friends in this world was our 10-year-old golden retriever, Justice. They were buds from Zoe's birth to the last moment of her life, and I believe that they are together now.

Zoe had a bone marrow transplant when she was seven months old to treat a rare blood disorder called HLH. This meant that post transplant she had to live on isolation for a year in order to give her new immune system a chance to grow and strengthen. Her social circle was small during this time, as germs were a big deal.

I had the distinct privilege of helping with looking after Zoe when she became ill until she was two-and-a-half. Walking Justice was a regular routine that we did together, and she loved it. Zoe's connection with animals was profound. It was as though she saw no separation between herself and them. She saw the beauty and magic in every creature, but her connection with Justice was truly incredible. They loved each other deeply.

After her transplant Zoe recovered slowly but surely. It was a hard road, but with her parents' incredible devotion and the love that surrounded her, combined with her own brave spirit, Zoe's body healed. She was able to live a "regular" life of school, play and adventure until just after her fourth birthday.

We were all having dinner one night and Zoe started slurring her words. We went to the hospital, and that was the moment when everything changed. They found numerous lesions in her brain. Eventually Zoe was diagnosed with T-cell non-Hodgkin's lymphoma of the CNS.

Zoe's first illness was rare. She was a 1-in-5-million baby. This cancer diagnosis was rarer still. Not a single case had been reported in a child before. Only adult protocols to follow.They did their best to treat her based on the little information that they had.

With grace, courage, and incredible heart, Zoe navigated five months of chemo and countless tests and scans until her little body surrendered; with her pal Justice beside her - along with her mom, dad, uncle and myself. Every room of the hospice was also full of people whose lives had been touched by Zoe's being - grandparents, aunts, uncles, cousins - family and friends who had helped care for her - all who loved her deeply. The staff at the hospice said they had never seen that level of support and love before.

As Zoe was dying, I longed to know and to feel where she was transitioning to, so that I could answer her honestly when she would tell me that she was scared and asked what was happening to her. I never wanted to lie to her, so I started reading books about near-death experiences. My answers to Zoe were always, *Your body is sick, darling. The doctors are trying to help you. But there is nothing to fear, we are right here with you and we love you so very much.*

We would look each other in the eyes and hold each other's faces and I would say, *Do you know how much I love you?* And she would answer, *To the moon and back.* We would hold each other tightly, like our souls knew how precious these embraces were.

In the last few days of her life I started to feel an energetic cord connecting us, as though our hearts were beating together. I felt oneness with her being like I had never known before in this life. And when her heart stopped beating, for weeks after, it felt like my heart was searching for hers.

Justice passed away two months after Zoe died, almost to the day.

After Zoe and Justice passed, it was as though I went into a cocoon. The world was too much, I had to be alone or with my "safe" people. The ones who knew this pain too. I was amazed at how friends we had had for years just wanted my life to go back to normal. Like there was this expectation just to snap back into action and socializing. I felt so angry and hurt by this and I retreated more.

I realized that I needed to learn how to hold myself in this pain and be the safest person for me to be with.

In the months that followed nature felt like the safest place for me. I longed for silence and being alone with the trees and animals. Often I would call Zoe's mom, Angela, and we would drink wine and cry and process the trauma of Zoe's suffering and the emptiness and longing that we both felt.

I struggled with letting go of the attachment that I felt to both Zoe and Justice. I felt angry, like someone had broken a promise to me that Zoe would live a long and healthy life. I have come to realize that no one actually made this promise to me, and she came for a short time, to teach us a profound lesson about living.

Zoe's life expanded my understanding of love to new heights. Her death cracked me open to new depths of pain and ache. I never knew I could love the way that I loved her.

Likewise, the physical and emotional pain of her passing has felt too much to bear. Many times I've thought it is impossible to carry on living with this amount of ache. I have wished many times that I could join her, where she is now. Many mornings I willed that I wouldn't wake up, but I did and I continue to. I keep putting one foot in front of the other and try to allow this pain I feel to be my teacher.

I am a firm believer now that cracks are how the light gets in. Losing Zoe splayed me wide open, and in the initial months following her passing I felt like my life and all of the pieces it was made of had crumbled to the ground. Every single aspect of my existence and how I had been living was up for re-evaluation.

Our grief social worker said, *It's as though throughout your life you build a lego castle of belief. When you lose a child or a loved one, the whole thing collapses. As you heal, you pick up each piece and decide if it still has a place in your castle.*

It has been one-and-a-half years since Zoe's passing, and this process of considering my life and how I am showing up in it continues.

At some point I decided that if I was going to stay living on this earth, then I was going to dive deep. I believe that Zoe's spirit is guiding me and has gifted me so many incredible people on my path to help me heal and get to know my true self in the process. I have found various types of breathwork, somatic healing, movement meditation, and yoga to be life-changing practices.

As a result of learning how to sit in the darkness and the light, I have uncovered layers of myself that I never knew before. I have been able to heal trauma and emotional pain that has been stored in my body my whole life.

64

I had been chronically ill for 16 years with Lyme disease. As a result of the deep body-mind-spirit healing work that I have been doing, I am living physically well for the first time in a very long while.

My husband and I struggled hard after Zoe's passing as well, as I realized that our grief processes differed greatly. But as we both allowed our pain and our healing to flow, as we both showed up and did our work and committed to sharing our process with one another, it's as though our 14-year relationship experienced a rebirth as well.

I have developed a relationship with my grief now. I try to check in with it daily.

I observe where I feel it in my body and listen to how it is asking to be felt and moved. Sometimes that looks like crying alone in the dark, sitting with my journal and pen, drinking wine, and reading poetry with Angela, adventuring with my husband or through dance, song, yoga, or sitting in silence in the forest. I have shifted to living in the present moment, trying to experience it fully, connecting to my breath and feeling my body.

This is what I have committed to. Unconditional openness, listening to my own inner guidance and feeling deeply all that this life has to offer. I am still here, and as long as I am, I will live and love with wild abandon, the way that Zoe taught me.

Fearless and Fancy and deeply rooted in love.

-Kylie Judge

65

I miss you

The nights are the hardest I find to bear
when all I can do is lay here and stare

The emptiness of what was once your space
how I long to see and touch your face

No longer does your body lay next to mine
our hearts no longer beat in perfect time.

It's these times I greet my familiar friend
his name is loneliness and it starts to descend

The darkness starts to gather round
I call out to you but you're nowhere to be found

It's at times like this I feel so alone
wanting to hear your voice that familiar tone

You said you'd never leave me
sadly it wasn't meant to be

I know it wasn't your choice you had to go
if it had been you'd clearly have said no

I must face life living without you now
some days I stand and wonder exactly how?

But go on I will without you here
even though at times I'm filled with fear

For you my love I promise to stay strong
I'll keep your memory going on

I'll stand tall and proud as your wife
continue to live a happy life.

Through the children I'll always see
the love we have you and me

In the darkness of the night
I'll look to my heart for the light

You are always there in that special place
my memories will show me your smiling face

I'll drift off to sleep the tears will subside
in my dreams I know you'll be by my side

Miss you babes.

-Kerry Knight

If time travel was possible, I'd want to go back to this. To home. To her.

Kathy, my mother.

She would invite the arrival of fall with open windows and an antique pot constantly simmering with cinnamon sticks, cloves, grapefruit, and orange peels.

I close my eyes and see that little old house that somehow survived the fiercest hurricanes. The giant popcorn tree by the back door is turning colors and dropping its leaves. The crab-back spiders are weaving around its branches.

If you walk down to the rocks and sit for a while, you'll hear the spouts of porpoises passing through the canal.

My mother has been dead for two-and-a-half years. I was nearing my twenty-seventh birthday. She was sixty years old.

I am plagued by questions I will never know the answers to, by the surprise of it all.

I had not hugged my mother in years. I had not spoken to her in weeks. I will never know what her final moments were like.

This grief has become medicine - what breaks me open, what heals me, what is showing me the way, what connects me to the sacred nature of all things, especially her.

And I am the keeper of what she knew, whether she knew it or not. Her green thumb, her attention and caregiving that brought life from the ground year after year. Her highly sensitive nature, needing quiet, needing support, needing kindness, most of all from herself. Her resilience, her compassion, her resourcefulness, her pride, her lack. The lessons she learned as a woman that she never shared, yet I secretly know and have experienced for myself. I receive her life-lived wisdom, now. I will carry our medicine.

 A friend recently mentioned how I have taught her to appreciate her own mother. What a gift. This is what I am learning: to open to grief is to open greater into love.

My mama told me several years ago that she felt at peace with leaving this world because she had done her job. She had raised us both to be capable adults, thus her job was finished, we would be ok.

But we all know a mother's job is never done. She's still here, despite what she may have thought about death.

She's everywhere - and she always will be.

- Candice Lyerla Jones

My Story

_____

_____

_____

_____

_____

_____

_____

_____

_____

_____

_____

_____

_____

_____

_____

_____

_____

_____

_____

_____

_____

Your story completes this book.

These pages are for you to tell the truth about your loved one or your grief through words, drawings, photos or mementos.

_____
_____
_____
_____
_____
_____
_____

What do you wish the world understood about your grief?

_____
_____
_____
_____
_____
_____
_____
_____
_____
_____
_____

Is there
something you
have never
said to
another
human being
about your
grief?

_____

_____

_____

_____

_____

_____

_____

_____

_____

_____

_____

_____

_____

_____

_____

_____

You're writing to tell the truth.
And you're writing to satisfy that part of you that says:
I have this truth to tell.

-Nikki Giovanni

PRACTICES

PART II

Grief is a practice, not a problem to fix.

A practice of holding on and letting go
of letting in and letting out
of falling and rising
of speaking and listening
of honoring and living
of trembling and soothing
of carving out a space for love and loss to coexist
in our heads and in our hearts.

A practice of being human.

Grief In The Body

Chapter I

The body is the first home for our grief, starting with the feeling of our hearts breaking.

Grief often tries to flow through our bodies and finds itself at an impasse or with no way out.

Words that crave to be heard or emotions that attempt to release are often pushed down into a lump in our throat.

Anger finds itself running in furious circles, voiceless and unheard.

Our gut instincts are ignored because its elegant alarm system is mistrusted.

Our bodies are the container for our every experience. They have intelligence and experience and support us and need support from us at every turn.

Have you ever had a gut feeling?

Has your heart felt like it was literally breaking or sinking?

Has your throat felt dry or tight when you were nervous?

Have you felt butterflies in your belly when you were nervous or excited?

If you have experienced any of the above, you have experienced the physiological sensations that accompany emotion moving through your body.

Emotions are a combination of energy mobilized in the body and the thoughts our minds assign to the sensations or feelings that accompany that mobilized energy.[1,2]

Grief is not just an emotion. It is a multidimensional experience that is biopsychosocial; meaning biological, psychological, and social factors affect our experience of grief.

Yet much of what we experience as grief is emotion.

Some of it we can name, such as sadness, anxiety, despondence, or depression.

Some of it we can't wrap words around, yet we can feel it under our skin, in our bones and in our hearts. We can feel our pounding or sinking heart, the lump in our throat, the knot in our bellies. We can feel the complexity and confusion of the feelings that have no names.

Our bodies often bear the burden of our grief, trying to manage all the sensations, feelings, emotions, and thoughts that accompany our grief.

Understanding how grief moves through the body in general can allow us to explore grief in our particular body and find ways to support its contraction, expansion, and harness our unique, heroic healing energies.

The following pages look at three different perspectives on emotion and sensation in the body: The BodyMind, the Vagus Nerve, and Traditional Chinese Medicine.

How Emotions Communicate

Much like we communicate with a friend over the phone about how we are feeling, many organs in our body, such as our lungs, heart, gut, liver, larynx and more communicate with our brain bidirectionally. [3]

The organs relay information to the brain about what they are sensing and experiencing, like when we tell our friend, "I lost my job," "I had a bad day," or "I am depressed."

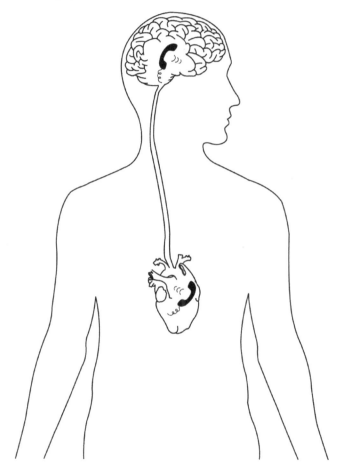

They also receive information from the brain, inviting the body to calm down, similar to when our friend responds, "It's going to be okay."

Sometimes our body's ancient and elegant communication system gets a little skewed by things that have happened to us and can send the wrong signals.

A little like a crank caller, creating alerts and alarm where there is no need. We can even disconnect completely because it is easier not to feel.

Taking a closer look at two bodies of research on this bidirectional communication gives us a better understanding of how this happens.

The BodyMind + The Vagus Nerve

The first concept is that of a BodyMind. Not just the body, not just the mind. A unified BodyMind.

The concept of a unified BodyMind is based on research done by neuropharmacologist Candace Pert, who discovered that many of our vital organs, including the sexual organs, are lined with receptors that communicate with the brain. [4]

She called these "molecules of emotion" and proposed that the density of these neuropeptides and receptors in places like the lining of our gut explain our "gut feeling." She also suggested that these molecules of emotion can get stuck in our body and are always seeking a way to move through the body and be expressed. [5]

The second body of research is into the vagus nerve.

The vagus nerve is an ancient nerve that runs from our brainstem to these same vital organs and more, informing the brain about what the body is experiencing. Up to 80 percent of the fibers of this nerve run from the organs to the brainstem. [6]

The vagus nerve has two branches, ventral and dorsal.

The ventral branch runs from the front of the brain stem to organs above the diaphragm, like the heart or lungs, and also innervates the facial, throat, and inner ear muscles.

The dorsal branch runs from the back of the brain stem to organs below the diaphragm, like the large and small intestine.

Together these two branches of the vagus nerve communicate the visceral experience of the organs - those physical and emotional internal sensations in our organs that are driven by physiological mechanisms like those "molecules of emotion" - to the brain. This allows us humans to not only self-regulate, but also co-regulate.

Science is continually confirming what we humans have always felt.

Our emotions often arise from and move through our bodies.

Traditional Chinese Medicine

Traditional Chinese Medicine (TCM) offers a unique perspective on emotions in the body by assigning certain emotions to certain organs in the body. [7]

Viewing the body holistically, TCM respects the inherent healing ability of every human body and every human being.

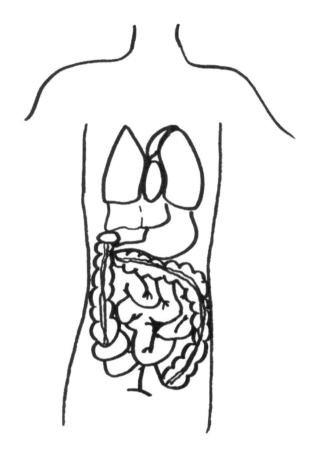

Practices that flow from this approach, such as acupuncture and herbalism, consider the physical body, the energetic body, and the emotional body in approaching illness, disease, and healing.

TCM assigns grief to a pair of organs: the Lungs and the Large intestine.

Joy, which also encompasses the loss of joy, is assigned to the Heart and the Small intestine.

These four organs - the heart, lungs, large and small intestine - hold and communicate significant information to the brain via the BodyMind receptors and the vagus nerve pathways discussed on the previous pages.

These three perspectives on emotions and grief in the body acknowledge and give credibility to the value of our feelings. The felt sense we often ignore or try to outthink.

When we understand the process and the places grief and its accompanying energy and emotions move through or may get stuck in our bodies, we can begin to investigate our own grief and how it may be showing up on any given day.

We can honor how it flows and intentionally support our body's efforts to heal. We can create awareness and space for it to move however and wherever it needs to on any given day.

Combining body awareness and knowledge with our mental efforts to find a way through our grief gives us more combined tools than either one alone and a more integrated approach to our grief.

There are multiple embodied therapies and practices that assist us in tuning in to our bodies, working with the energy of grief, and supporting the process of integrating our grief and our love, our loss, and our life.

One of these is yoga, which we will explore at length in Chapter III.

Organs of Grief

Chapter II

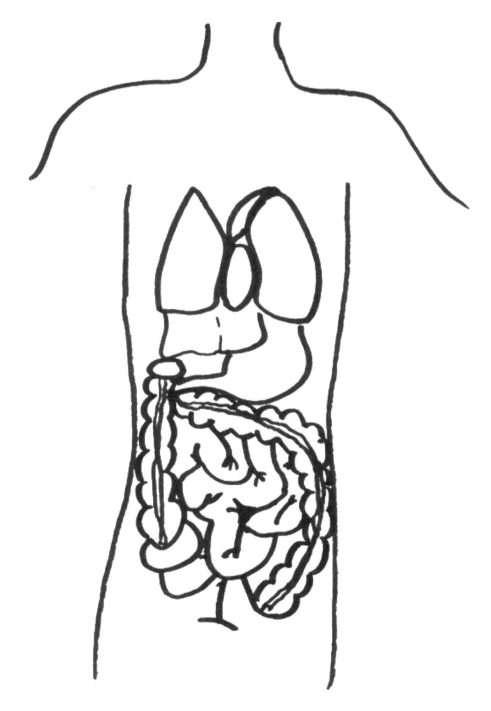

Our Lungs are the way our bodies take in air. The way we take in life.

When grieving it is normal to feel as if we have lost all will to live. If our bodies didn't breathe for us, we might not have the energy or the will to breathe.

Energetically the lungs can feel weighed down with unbearable sadness. Physically we might feel pain in this part of our bodies, have difficulty breathing, or develop respiratory illnesses or issues. Emotionally the Lungs are the yin organ assigned to grief and sadness in Traditional Chinese Medicine.

The Lungs communicate what they are experiencing to the brain via the vagus nerve and neuroreceptors discussed in the previous section on Grief In The Body.

The Lungs are the container for our breath and for our life. We can support our body's efforts to heal by approaching the lungs and breath in a few different ways.

On a physical level we can create more space for the breath and ease when breathing by working with the diaphragm (page 127), strengthening and stretching our intercostal muscles (page 147), working with some of the accessory breathing muscles (page 142), breath awareness (page 156), and inviting the body into shapes that support an expansive, natural inhale and exhale.

While breathing is largely an autonomic and automatic process, meaning our bodies breathe on their own, we also have the ability to voluntarily direct and control our breath, which can improve its function.

Becoming aware of our breath in different ways allows us to use it as an anchor. Regulating our breath directly impacts our heart rate. [8]

Ultimately our lungs are generous holders of life, can struggle under the weight of our grief, and remind us that everything is cyclical, contracting and expanding. Just like our grief.

Our Hearts are the first home for our grief, starting with the moment we feel them break or collapse in our chests. It lands here, the news, the struggle, the goodbyes we exchanged or never got to say.

How we feel, good or bad, affects the physiological state of our heart, creating heart rhythms that are scrambled or ones that are more coherent. [9]

Bathing the literal heart in positive thoughts and feelings has been shown to improve heart rate variability, a key player in overall health and longevity. [10]

In addition to being impacted by our feelings and thoughts, our hearts are affected by our breath. Our inhales speed up our heart rate and our exhales slow them down. These fluctuations in our heart rate are an indicator of good heart-rate variability, a strong indicator of health and well-being.

Traditional Chinese Medicine assigns joy, and the lack of joy, to the heart. The expression "losing heart" speaks directly to the energy and aliveness the heart is the container for. Feeling empty-hearted or like our heart is literally breaking is common when grieving.

The physical sensations we experience in the heart are communicated to the brain via the vagus nerve, the BodyMind neuroreceptors, as well as the heart's "brain."

The heart's brain is a network of sophisticated nerves that can sense, process, and even make decisions. [11]

We are affected by our own heart energy as well as that of other humans, as our hearts have an energetic field that extends up to eight to ten feet. [12]

People heal people. When we engage in authentic, meaningful connections, even briefly or with total strangers, to our bodies these interactions feel like love. Yes, love! [13]

This kind of love and connection can be a soothing salve to the deep loneliness that often accompanies grief, as even perceived loneliness has physiological consequences. [14]

Since the heart can be highly charged, both positively and negatively, keeping this in mind as we explore our grief can guide us in choosing what supports our process. Sometimes tuning into the heart can feel supportive and healing. Sometimes it can feel overwhelming and scary.

Just like our bodies breathe automatically, our hearts beat automatically. And we can affect our heart rate and function through breath awareness, authentic connections, and heart-centered practices. [15] [16]

Our hearts have never left our side, not even for a moment. They are generous with their phenomenal ability to heal from even the most tragic and devastating experiences.

Our Intestines are the home of our "gut feelings."

Physically, the intestines are the part of our body involved in digestion, moving things through and letting things out. Processing our grief and all that we have lost can feel difficult and sometimes impossible.

Sometimes moving things through on a physical level can be problematic as well. Intestinal distress can manifest as digestive problems such as gastric pain or constipation.

Energetically we might sense fear or feel disconnected from this area of the body.

Emotionally the outer, large intestine is the yang organ assigned to grief in Traditional Chinese Medicine, while the inner, small intestine is the partner organ for joy and the lack of joy.

Our intestines, just like the heart, have their own "brain," made up of a network of neurons lining the walls of these organs. Part of this enteric nervous system or "brain" is the BodyMind neuroreceptors. Much of the communication between this "brain" in our gut and the "brain" in our heads happens through the vagus nerve. [17] [18] [19]

Emotionally and energetically processing and supporting our grief extends beyond our physical bodies and minds. How our families, communities, and society receive and support our grief deeply impacts our experience of grief.

Feeling societal pressure to "resolve" our grief in a finite period of time or package it up in a way that is acceptable and digestible to other people can be unsettling to our gut sense that this experience has changed us forever and may accompany us for the rest of our life.

When we access this part of the body through our core muscles, such as the abdominal muscles, we create a literal "felt sense" of strength and connection to ourselves. [20] Certain movements, such as twists, can nourish the fascia, muscles, and nerves around the intestines. Our breath can also help calm the viscera in this area, sending the message to the intestines that we are safe and everything is okay in this moment.

Removing some of the pressure to rush through our grief or force ourselves to let go of something when we are not ready to can allow us to process our grief in our own way, in our own time, remembering that there is no right way to grieve. There is just our way.

And sometimes we don't have to let it go. We just have to let it out.

Our Throats are the gateway. They are a primary outlet for communication.

The throat can be a key area of the body impacted by grief. It is easy to overlook this area because many of us have grown up in a society that taught us to hold things in from an early age.

The throat is the way we express ourselves. Physically, the throat contains the larynx, an organ in our necks that contains our vocal cords.

When we restrain our expression or our emotion (e.g. the lump in the throat) we restrict the flow of both the emotion and the energy of grief.

The emotions of grief, just like the emotions of love or anger, crave freedom to flow. Sometimes in, sometimes out, but freedom to take up space.

Often we may feel no one wants to hear what we have to say related to our grief or that there is no one to express our grief to. Finding a throat-related practice can help move the energy of grief through the body.

Singing in a church choir or in the shower, crying, chanting in a yoga class or singing along at your favorite concert are all effective ways to tune into this area of the throat.

Singing, chanting, or even humming require slow exhalations as well as controlled shifting of the facial muscles. Think about what happens to your face when you sing your favorite song.

These slow exhalations slow down our heart rate, creating a sense of calm in the body, while simultaneously "exercising" our facial, middle ear, and larynx muscles. Combined, this creates what is called a Heart-Face connection, a powerful way to regulate the body and stimulate the vagus nerve. [21] [22]

The unique way you find to invite and allow the energy of the throat to move may not feel related to your grief at all. It doesn't have to.

The intelligence of the body is not linear and compartmentalized. It knows how to heal if we let it.

Crying feels

Tears

Sometimes
we feel better after a good cry
because crying can help to regulate
our bodies by both arousing
and calming our nervous system.

In this way crying can be a form of self-soothing. [23]

Just like we humans respond when people smile at us,
we also respond when someone cries.
Crying activates our social engagement system in a similar way,
inviting other humans to offer comfort or care.

Crying in grief can also cause headaches and other aches and pains.

Even though our culture has a dismissive attitude towards physical pain and
encourages a "suck it up" mentality, finding ways to nourish what is depleted when
crying can help to support our bodies as they negotiate the physical demands of
grieving.

Taking in more fluids, including electrolyte-fortified drinks, can help to replenish our
bodies when we find ourselves having frequent bouts of crying.

While allowing the emotions and energy related to our grief to have a free-flowing
outlet like crying can be a powerful healing tool, sometimes crying can cause
immense amounts of pain in the body.

In those cases it can be helpful to explore other ways to work
with the enormous energy of grief through the body,
such as shaking, swinging, breathing techniques,
and titrated movement so that the energy mobilized
by our experience of grief can have additional
outlets beyond tears.

Map Your Grief

Where we sense our grief in our bodies changes from day to day. The organs we have discussed are a starting place. Your grief may or may not manifest in any of the organs mentioned. Your grief is unique to you and your body. This is why it can be useful to map your own grief.

To scan your body for grief, settle into a place and space you feel safe and supported. Choose a position that feels right to you.

Notice how your body feels right now, without changing anything.

Your eyes may be open or closed. Sense the parts of your feet that are in contact with the ground. Squeeze your leg muscles to deepen the connection to your body.

Maintain that connection with your feet and legs as you invite your grief in, to be seen and felt by you. This can be through a memory of your loved one while they were alive or recalling how you felt in the days or months after they died. Choose a memory or visual that feels manageable to you in this moment.

Keep your attention more in the body, less on the story that accompanies the memory. Look for sensations that arrive or arise or for parts of your body, inner and outer, that may shift. Keep noticing what sensations arise in your body for a few moments.

What, if anything, shifted in your body, subtly or obviously? Did your breath change? Did your facial muscles tense or soften? Did your shoulders lift or did your chest collapse? Did you feel an energetic shift in your heart or belly?

Draw or color in on the body diagrams on the following pages the areas you noticed or sensed.

This map allows you to acknowledge and honor
the beautiful job your heart and mind
are doing with what they have,
where you have come from,
and what you are
dealing with.

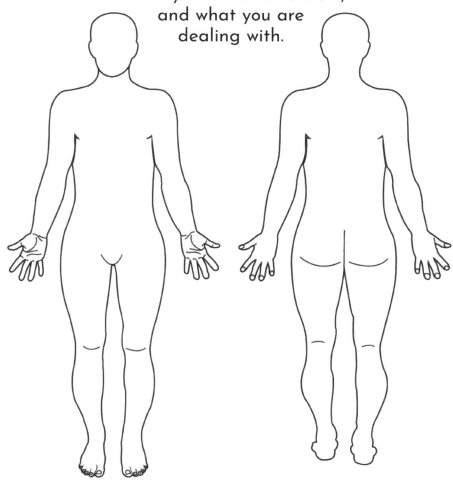

Rest here, in the knowledge your body and mind are doing the best they can. Or use the simple, embodied tools in this book to support the efforts of your body and mind.

Rather than being a map of what is "wrong," allow this to be a map of what IS.

Your body and mind are doing everything they can to keep you functioning and healing at their own pace.

Our bodies and minds are always working to regulate us, keep us upright and alive, whatever it takes. That is something to celebrate.

Scanning and mapping our grief can bring up some powerful sensations. Finding a way to discharge the energy that's been mobilized can act as a "reset button" for our bodies and minds. Shaking and tremoring the body is one of the most natural and powerful regulating resources we humans have. [24]

Here are 3 ways to discharge the energy that's been mobilized. Perhaps you can add to this list something that feels better to you, like dancing or swimming or singing.

Swinging. Sit on an exercise ball and rock back and forth in a swinging motion.

Bouncing. Stand comfortably and begin to bounce. Invite the knees to move, perhaps the hips.

Shake + Exhale. Stand comfortably and begin with bouncing. Increase the speed until the bouncing becomes more of a shaking. Add in the arms, the hands, maybe even the head. Watch your breath. It may naturally shift with the movement. Follow its lead. Alternatively, see what it feels like to take big, open-mouth exhales.

After your movement of choice, sit down into a squat or on a chair and take some long exhales, imagining the breath moving down through your body and into the earth.

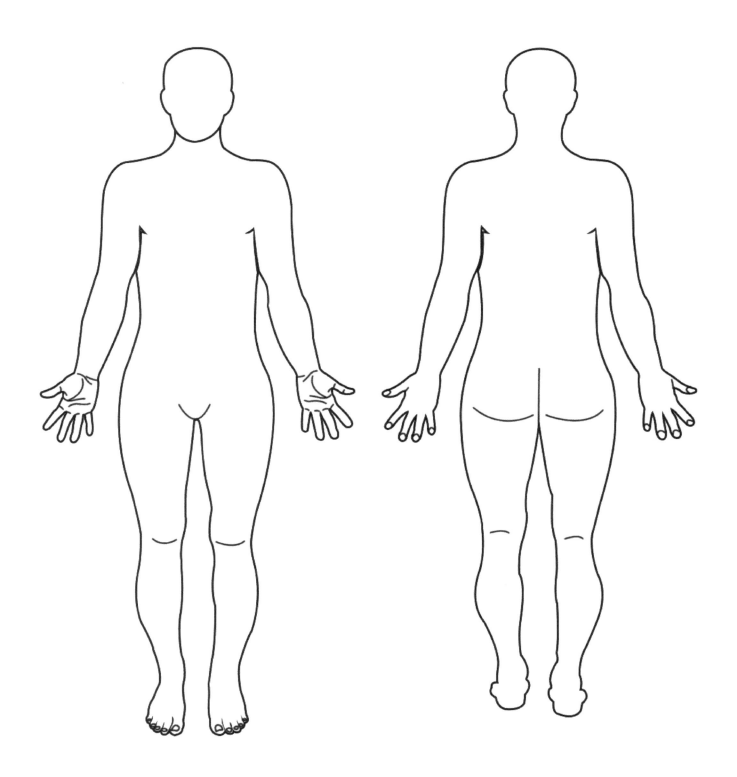

Download and print additional body maps and find the Shake & Ground video at
TheGriefPractice.com.

What if your grief could take up this much space?

What if you could walk through your day and not have to hide your grief, not have to struggle to "keep it together" because people don't understand, not have to push your grief down, make it small, hidden, or act like it doesn't exist?

What would it feel like in your body to be this supported in your grief, this entitled to your feelings, to create this expansive of a container for your grief?

What would that look like for you, in your body?

What would that feel like for you, in your body?

Maybe you stand in a doorway and feel it out for yourself.

Maybe you imagine yourself standing in a doorway or taking up a whole room or a whole city or the whole world.

Maybe you make this experiment and experience completely your own.

Maybe you slowly move from a small, curled-up position to standing tall and find somewhere in between small and large, hidden and seen, closed and open that feels supportive and good to you in your body today.

Take the next two blank pages to draw or express what this feels like to you.

Yoga

Chapter III

Yoga is often sought out as a means to fix things, like back pain or stress. However, when it comes to grief, there is nothing to fix.

There is nothing wrong with your grief.
There is nothing wrong with you.
You are having a tremendous human experience.

It is common to feel surges of emotion during a yoga practice. The first year I practiced yoga, several years after my husband's death, I found myself crying in the final resting pose at the end of each class.

When we breathe, chant, or move our bones and muscles in yoga, we impact organs. Many of these are the same organs affected by our experience of grief, as we have discussed.

When we bring our awareness to our bodies, when we move our bodies with intention and attention, we invite grief to take up space, to move, to surge or recede, to flow. We allow it to be whatever it needs to be without rushing, crowding, or denying it.

Grief, especially traumatic grief, can literally change the parts of our brain that light up and communicate with each other. [25]

To borrow an analogy from Dr. Dan Siegel, imagine your brain as a house. Your "upstairs brain," the neocortex, is where critical thinking, problem-solving, and good decision-making happens. Your "downstairs brain," the limbic system, is where necessary functions like breathing, the fight/flight/freeze response, and powerful emotions live. [26]

Our brains also have a left and right hemisphere. The left hemisphere controls the right side of our body. The right hemisphere controls the left side of our body.

Understanding this helps us see how movement and mindfulness can have a whole-brain effect and support our entire BodyMind experience of grief.

The movement and breath practices of yoga are a bottom-up approach to the brain, working at the level of the "downstairs brain." [27]

Talk therapy is an example of a top-down approach, working with the "upstairs brain," capable of rationalizing, creating stories and structure around our experiences.

Mindfulness, the practice of paying attention to what's happening right now, is also top-down, occuring in the medial prefrontal cortex. [28]

When we recruit the left and right hemispheres of the brain through cross-lateral movement, such as twisting or using both sides of our body at the same time in different ways or breathwork such as alternate nostril breathing (see page 157), we invite the left and right sides of our brain to communicate more fluidly. [29]

By blending mindful attention with intelligent movement we gain the benefit of both top-down and bottom-up approaches, as well as more harmonious left and right hemispheres.

In other words, we invite our whole brain to light up and support our whole body's efforts to integrate our pain, our loss, and honor its innate desire and ability to heal.

We often turn to yoga as something to help us find peace or feel better, yet we can sometimes feel worse as our grief begins to move through our bodies.

It can show up as a range of feelings arising "out of nowhere," such as anger, intense sadness, or confusion.

This can feel surprising, overwhelming, or make us feel like our yoga is not working.

Remember, feeling worse does not always mean we are doing worse.*

Often our practice is freeing up emotions that may have been stored or stuck in our bodies for years, perhaps even predating or unrelated to our grief. [30]

Navigating grief in the body, whether we encounter it accidentally or intentionally, is easier when we have anchors to hold onto so we aren't as easily swept away by our emotions, memories, or thoughts.

* Always contact a mental healthcare professional if you begin to feel depressed or have suicidal thoughts.

Anchors

An anchor on a boat does not stop the storm from coming. It does not stop the boat from rocking. It does not stop the waves from crashing overboard.

An anchor keeps the boat from being swept away.

Using anchors in yoga does not stop grief. It does not stop us from feeling pain, sadness, or any other emotion.

It gives us something to hold onto when our emotions, memories, or thoughts start to sweep us away.

Before each practice you are invited to choose an anchor to work with. It might be one suggested here or something of your own creation.

Of the anchors discussed here, one may feel more natural than the others at any given time. Start with that one.

Use the anchors in the way that supports your process best. You might focus all or most of your attention on your anchor to start and then adjust from there.

The anchors can be used in conjunction with any yoga practice, whether supported or active, by shifting your attention back and forth between your anchor and the sensations you feel in your body, like a pendulum; whether that be physical or emotional pleasure or discomfort, a sense of mental or emotional connection or numbness, or intense sensation. Use the anchor to allow you to observe the temporary nature of each feeling, emotion, or sensation from one practice to the next.

After integrating anchors into your yoga practice in this way, you may wish to practice using your anchors and pendulating skills in your everyday life when you feel overwhelmed by feelings, memories, or sensations.

Try connecting to one or all of the following anchors right now, wherever you are, starting at the top.

Note that the breath is intentionally listed last. For some people the breath can feel destabilizing and agitating. Use the first anchors to create a container before exploring the breath until using the breath as an anchor feels natural and easy.

Look Around

Look around your space like it is the first time you have been here.
Look for texture and color.
Look for shadow and light.
If you are in a room with people, notice who is standing or sitting next to you.
Let your gaze rest on something that catches your attention.

Listen For Sounds

Tune in to your sense of hearing.
Listen for the farthest sound you can hear.
Move in from there to the next closest sound you can hear.
Keep moving in from there, sound by sound.

Feel The Ground

What parts of your body are touching the floor or are being supported?
(e.g. the bottom of your feet or your sitz bones supported by a chair.)
Can you deepen this connection by contracting the muscles around these body
parts and pressing them into those supports?

Find Your Center

What feels like your center today?
(It might be your center of gravity. It might be a part of your body like your belly
or heart or throat. It might be someone or something outside of you that makes
you feel centered.).
What does it feel like to be centered?

Notice Your Breath

What does the breath feel like in your nostrils on the inhale?
Does it feel cool or warm?
Begin to notice which nostril the breath is more dominant in right now.
Which is longer, your inhale or your exhale?

The first three anchors - looking, listening, and grounding - ask us to notice external stimuli, what we see, hear, and feel outside.

The next two anchors ask us to notice internal sensations; finding a center point and noticing our breath.

Becoming familiar with all the anchors allows us to be able to switch our attention to the most useful one in any given moment. If focusing on our internal sensations (anchors four and five) or any other physical sensation starts to feel overwhelming, we can switch our attention to focus on external stimuli (anchors one through three) until we feel more in control of our experience. [31]

Once we are familiar with each anchor, we can use them to support our experience in a yoga practice by choosing the amount of attention we put on the anchor and the amount of attention we put on the sensations, emotions, or thoughts that may come up in our practice. Some days we may need to focus more attention on the anchor and less on the sensations. Other days we may find we can go exploring more of our sensations or emotions, knowing our anchors are there to keep us grounded as we explore or help us find our way back if we start to get overwhelmed.

In yoga classes we are often cued to close our eyes or direct our gaze inward. Know you always have the right to keep your eyes open or look around your space if this feels more grounding or safe to you. [32]

Using anchors in our day-to-day life is a similar process. When thoughts arise that are overwhelming, these embodied anchors can serve as "islands of safety," or ways we can ground ourselves and things we anchor our attention to as we survive, explore, or surrender to whatever may be coming up for us. [33]

Supported Shapes

Our experience of grief can feel so devastating and depleting at times that we may not have the energy for big movement. Even when we can do something, it doesn't mean we should. It may further deplete our already exhausted nervous systems or physical energy.

This is where supported shapes, or restorative postures, can be useful.

These shapes allow the body to deeply rest while also gaining the benefit of the shapes. They allow us to "try on" new shapes and sensations in the body in a gentle, unforced way, allowing our nervous systems to acclimate to new or different ranges of motion slowly and safely. [34]

Feeling safe is the bottom line when it comes to creating opportunities for healing in our bodies.

When we don't feel safe our bodies move into a defensive, protective state. While in this state it is difficult to soften or heal. [35]

Much of what makes us feel unsafe are cues from our environment or the people in our environment, like someone's tone of voice, facial expression, or unexpected, loud, or low-frequency sounds. [36]

This quality of neuroception, where our nervous systems evaluate risk without our being aware of it, goes a long way to how comfortable and safe we feel.

Keeping this in mind when choosing how and where to practice yoga can help us create a practice that is best suited for where we are and how we are in this moment.

Choose a location where you feel comfortable and safe. Gather the props you may need beforehand so you don't have to get up and down and disturb the experience.

1. This shape creates opening along the front of the body and arranges the head so it's lower than the heart, increasing vagal tone. [37]

2/3. This shape allows gentle opening along the front of the body; the belly, chest, and throat. It also provides support for the paraspinal muscles. This support along the back of the body allows the front of the body to experience an expanded and open shape.

4. This supported twist may be felt in the belly, low back, neck, or hip area. Arrange your neck to whichever side feels easeful.

5. The gentle inversion often has a calming effect. Inversions can increase vagal tone and stimulate the rest-and-digest function of the nervous system.

6. This shape creates a generous lift in the upper chest. Increase or decrease the size of the roll until the front-body opening feels supportive and not forceful.

7. Use a bolster or roll up two pillows tightly in a towel or blanket. Keep another pillow or blanket handy. When you lie over the prop notice if the low or mid belly need more support. If so, place additional pillows or blankets where needed until resting over the props feels supportive.

1. Place a big book or block under your sacrum (the triangular bone between the hip sockets.)

Or

2. Fold the blanket in threes and sit at the end so your tailbone is just off the edge.

3. Lie back onto the support.

4. Line up the middle of one hip with the center of the prop. Lengthen and lay the spine over the prop.

5. The distance you place your hips from the wall will depend on how your hamstrings feel.

6. Roll up a towel or blanket and place it lengthwise under the shoulder blades.

7. Place the prop between the legs, resting the belly, chest and head over the prop.

Yoga shapes have an energy to them.

Looking at Shapes 6 and 7, we can see how the supported chest opener might feel more exposed than the supported folded pose, Shape 7.

At different points in grief something like a front-body opener may or may not feel supportive or inviting. The energy of grief, especially initially, is often collapsed and exhausted. Closed shapes like the folded pose may feel safer and better depending on our body and the energy of our grief on any given day.

While inviting front-body opening may be just what we need to create some space and opening, there is a lot to be said for honoring the collapse. For letting our hearts and bodies contract, withdraw, steep in darkness, and learn our pain.

Often we rise before we are ready because if we didn't we might stay down forever. This is how we survive.

Sometimes years or even decades later we have the support or circumstances to revisit parts of our grief we rushed or held our breath through in our effort to survive.

You are the conductor of your own experience.
Choose what feels right to you.

Diaphragm Release To Free Up Breathing

Our bodies do the best they can to hold up under the weight of our grief. The lungs can take a major hit. Often people complain of feeling like they cannot take a full breath. This diaphragm release is a way to create more access to the breath.

The goal of all the props in this shape is to create enough support for the low back to be resting on the floor (in a posterior tilt.)

This allows us to access our thoracic diaphragm, a major breathing muscle, in a different way than when we're upright and it is functioning as a skeletal muscle.

Once you have supported yourself enough so that your low back is resting on the ground without effort, take a normal inhale, a normal exhale, and then another exhale, pushing all the air out.

This double exhale fully contracts the diaphragm, allowing the lungs to receive the maximum amount of air on the inhale without extra effort.

Try it a few times and notice how the air fills your chest cavity and how your breathing might shift from this practice.

Thank your body for its valiant efforts.
Thank yourself for supporting its efforts.

Sample Supported Sequence 1

Creating a sequence is simply a matter of choosing two or three poses and carving out enough time to rest for 5 to 10 minutes in each shape.

For the sample sequence on the opposite page I've chosen one from each category of supportive shapes. A closed shape, a front-body opener, and a twist. The twist will be done on each side, so allow for 10 to 20 minutes total to do the twist on both sides.

The idea with a sequence like this is to first start with something that feels familiar and safe. This supported folded pose invites us into a physical shape that feels safe and protected, and guides our attention back to a still and settled place.

Inviting some opening to the front of the body can be an optimal shape to work with the energy of the heart and counter the dominant shape of grief.

Twisting brings some sensation and awareness to the belly, the home of our intestines, creating some constriction in the belly and spinal muscles, as well as restricting the space available for breath. Notice the space and ease of breath before the twist, during the twist, and after the twist. Breathe into the space available.

Ideally after any sequence, supported or active, there is a few minutes left for a final resting shape, resting either on your back, side, or belly (shown on pages 130 and 131.) This *savasana* allows the body to absorb and integrate the practice.

Use the blank space on the photos or the lines on this page to note down any thoughts or feelings after trying the sequence or create your own.

If it feels right to you, find a gentle humming in this shape on the exhale. Let the inhale rebound naturally and then hum on the exhale.

To add a visualization tool, imagine the humming sound is coming from the center of your literal heart.

Find more sample practices and videos at TheGriefPractice.com

Gentle pressure on the abdomen can be soothing to our nervous system and calm the viscera in this area.

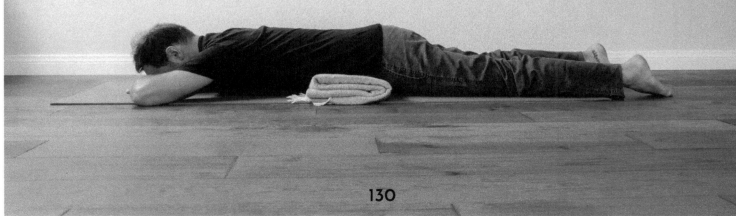

For your final resting shape choose something that feels good, supported, and safe to you.

This may be different each time depending on your energetic and emotional state, as well as how the movement and breathwork have affected your being.

Some ideas are offered on the opposite page, or choose something altogether different that feels right to you in this moment.

Active Shapes

Small movements can create a big shift when our bodies haven't moved in a while or when we are struggling under the weight of our grief.

Movement is a wonderful way to reconnect with the strength of our bodies, increase our "movement vocabulary," and strengthen our interoception, or awareness of what's happening inside the body. [38] The more we can notice what's happening inside, the more we are able to mobilize when needed to create change. When we experience and learn inner resilience and strength on a physical level, it often becomes easier to apply those skills to other aspects of our lives and our grief.

Mindfully incorporating movement that elevates our heart rate can allow our bodies to discharge some of the big energy that can get pent up in our bodies in grief through unexpressed or unacknowledged anger, frustration, and/or the other stresses that often accompany grief.

This is known as stress-cycle completion. Sometimes humans find intense styles of yoga very satisfying for certain times in their grief, although this discharge of energy can be accomplished with any activity that raises our heart rates while maintaining mindful attention.

Find more sample practices and videos at TheGriefPractice.com

These movements create some mobility in the shoulders and through the length of the spine.

On an exhale lift the hips and extend the arms overhead as far as feels comfortable for the shoulders.

Keep the arms overhead and begin to lower the spine slowly down, as if each vertebrae could move independently.

Bring the block back to the belly and repeat 4 or 5 rounds, resting and noticing between each cycle.

Creating a felt sense of connecting to our literal core can return our sense of agency in our own bodies. This may be useful in grief, a time when we sometimes feel eviscerated quite literally.

Our abdomens and the organs they hold communicate with our brain whether things feel safe, stressful, or scary.

Dropping into this level of the body takes advantage of our ability to send soothing message to the brain from these organs, reconnect with our literal strength, and touch in with our physical core and center.

Cross-lateral shapes and moving mindfully can invite parts of our brain that may have gone offline due to our grief to come back online.

This starfish-looking shape is easy way to invite the left and right hemispheres of the brain to sync up.

Lie on your back with arms and legs wide like a starfish (above left.)

On an exhale, cross the left arm over the right arm and the right leg over the left leg (above right.).

Hug it in to center (left.)

Open it back up to the starfish.

Now cross the right arm over the left and the left leg over the right.

Hug it in to center.

Repeat 2 more times, alternating arms and legs.

1. Draw the right knee in towards the chest without using the hands.

2. Press the heel to the sky, lengthening the leg.

3. Draw the knee in towards the chest.

4. Lengthen the leg out and hover it above the floor.

The movements on the opposing page use the strength of the leg muscles to facilitate movement, tuning us into our core strength and drawing our attention to the grounding energy of the lower body.

Start lying on your back with knees bent, feet flat on the floor.

Complete the sequence two or three times on the right side and then switch over to the left side.

If you are using an anchor, notice which one feels most natural in this shape and with this movement. See what it feels like to pulse your attention between your anchor and the sensations that may arise in your hips or legs.

You may wish to sync up your inhales and exhales with each movement or not. Choose what is best for you today.

1. Rest the foot on the block. Try to keep the hips stacked when you begin to move.

2. Slowly, like you're moving through thick honey, begin to lift and lower the leg, tapping the block.

3. Draw the top elbow down towards the ground.

4. Lift the elbow off the floor as you twist open.

Come to lying on your left side. Stack the palms together if that feels comfortable on your shoulders or position the arms however feels best. If syncing up one breath per movement feels right to you, incorporate the breath.

1/2. Lengthen out your bottom, left leg straight and extend your top, right leg in front of you, resting the foot on the block.

Use your top arm to feel the back of your hips, noticing how one hip is likely stacked right on top of the other. Try to maintain the hips stacked as you begin to move, isolating the movement to the leg instead of letting the pelvis move with it.

Recruiting strength and loading our joints and muscles through movements like this sends positive information from the receptor cells around the joints to the brain that things "feel" safe and strong and supports overall brain health. [39]

3/4. Draw the block in until the right knee can rest on it. Use your bottom hand to stabilize the top leg and place the top hand behind the head. After pulsing open and closed a few time, try pausing in an open twist for a few breaths.

Turn over to your right side and repeat.

141

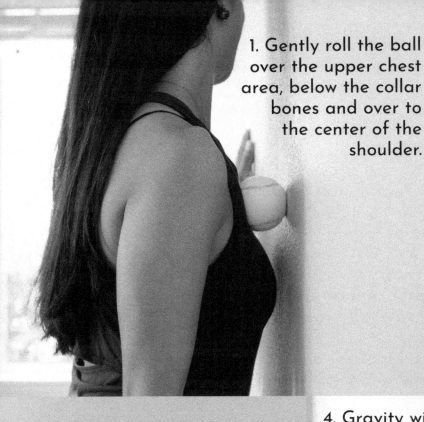

1. Gently roll the ball over the upper chest area, below the collar bones and over to the center of the shoulder.

2. Extend the arm and lift and lower the arm a few times.

3. Bring one arm behind the head and one behind the back without trying to reach the hands together.

Switch back and forth a few times.

4. Gravity will create a downward pull in this shape. Respond by lifting the armpits and drawing the front ribs down.

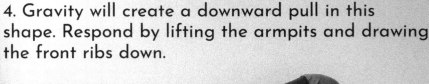

5. Lift and lower the block towards the back of the head or upper back a few times.

Pause with the block lifted, keeping the lift throughout the body you created in Shape 4 above.

The movements on the opposite page warm up the shoulder joints for this downward facing dog, while also countering the postural effects of grief.

Sometimes this can feel good to our bodies. Sometimes this can feel like too much or even scary. Proceed mindfully.

The upper chest is home to many accessory muscles that support breathing. We have nerve endings and fascia that respond to things like massage or this technique of rolling over a ball.

Providing stimulation in this area (Photo 1/2) can calm our nervous system in addition to supporting ease in breathing. Use gentle pressure to roll over the ball. Pressing hard creates more inflammation and puts the body in a defensive state.

Bringing the arms overhead, into external rotation (Photo 5) counters the shoulder position we experience in grief while keeping a protective container around the front of the body by keeping it close and in contact with the ground.

Bringing the head below the heart stimulates our vagus nerve which tells the body "everything is going to be okay."

When we force our bodies into a shape they can do but don't energetically or emotionally feel safe in, our bodies instinctively move into a defensive mode.

You are invited to
say the name of
your loved one,
out loud or to
yourself.

Sample Active Sequence 1

Lengthen your spine.

RT foot forward, cross arms across your chest or reach to the sky.

Twist to the right using your core.

What would make this shape feel better? Hands or knees wider or narrower?

Extend the RT leg and LT arm. Find balance.

Hug the arm/leg in toward each other.

Bend the RT knee, make 5 to 10 small, slow stomps up to the ceiling.

Extend the arms forward.

Rest. Repeat sequence on the other side.

What texture do you feel under your feet?

What parts of your skin feel warm? Cool?

Bring the right leg forward.

Hold steady or pulse, lifting and lowering the left knee to the ground.

Repeat the shapes on these two pages on the left side.

Extend the RT leg to the right. Reach the RT arm over to the left.

Lengthen from the outer right foot to the right armpit.

Notice the strength of the bottom shoulder lifting up in the shape.

Can you sense your top fingers in space?

Hold the shape above.

OR

Lift the bottom arm up and frame the ears.

Feel the steadiness of your legs and the strength of your core.

Bring the RT arm down the RT thigh.

Reach the LT arm to the sky for a counter stretch.

Breathe into each lung. Which one feels spacious? Which one feels contracted?

Can you breathe into the space available on the contracted side?

The shapes on the opposite page invite you to connect to a felt sense of strength in the upper back while also creating expansion across the front of the chest.

Choose the version that best meets your body and energy where it is today or progress through all three versions.

Root down through the pelvis and contract the glute muscles.
Drag the forearms toward the feet without moving the arms.

Squeeze the legs together, grab elbows or clasp hands. Peel up head, neck, chest.
Perhaps lift the legs while rooting down through the pelvis.

For the last couple breaths release the clasp of the hands while continuing to work
the shoulder blades towards each other, recruiting active strength and stability.

This active bridge pose is an energizing shape that invites an expansive opening through the front body.

Hold on to the sides of mat or use another arm variation.

Drag the heels towards the head without moving the feet.

Can you spread out the effort so no one part is doing all the work?

To incorporate some vocalization here, see what it feels like to make an SSSSSSS sound on your exhale.

To move into this active inversion, start in a supported bridge pose (page 123.)

With the block under your sacrum, bring both legs up towards the sky.
You may need to readjust the block a few times until it feels just right with the legs lifted.

You might wrap your hands around the block or find a different way that works best for your arms.

The legs may shake with the effort of holding themselves up.

Stay here anywhere from 15 seconds to several minutes.

Bend the knees as you come down or keep the legs extended to sense more of your core at work.

Find a gazing point to rest your sight on or use the breath as an anchor by counting backwards on the exhale from 10 to 1.

Start in a tabletop shape, on hands and knees.

Reach the right arm to the sky and weave it through and under the left arm.

Pulse in and out a few times before threading the right arm completely through.

Rest the right side of your head on the ground.

Walk the left fingertips forward to make more space.

Twisting shapes mobilize the abdomen, the muscles of the rib cage and spine and can stimulate the vagus nerve.

Use your core muscles to pulse the legs over to the RT, back to center, over to the LT a few times before resting in the twist.

After twisting on both sides, hug your head and knees into your chest.

Choose a final resting shape from page 130 and allow yourself 3 to 5 minutes to be still and allow your body to digest and assimilate all the information and movement it has just experienced.

Pause here, at this intersection of whatever is coming and whatever has been, and acknowledge your inherent wholeness which includes your broken parts.

Thank you for showing up for you.

Meditation

Once we have created a grounded and supported feeling in our bodies, meditation can be a wonderful support in grief.

When practicing any kind of meditation or yoga, it can be helpful to keep in mind our rights. Regardless of what any teacher or style or lineage says, these are things we are always entitled to, to keep these practices supportive and healthy.

Keep your eyes open
Look around
Take breaks
Change positions
Get up and walk
Shift your attention if you feel yourself disconnecting, feeling afraid or anxious
Say NO to touch or scents
Stay responsive to the signals or alarms from your body
Pendulate your attention between your internal awareness and your external awareness
Imagine you are in a place or with someone or something that feels safe or good
Get up and leave [40]

Meditation has been shown to activate an area of our brain that can step back and keep a bigger perspective on our particular situation. Activating this area of the brain, the medial prefrontal cortex, [41] can be a wonderful support in grief, allowing us to gain a broader perspective and an ability to integrate our loss into our life.

Humming Bee Breath

An ancient
meditation to suppor
the energy of the
heart.

Close both ears.
On an exhale begin
humming.
Inhale normally.
Hum on the exhale
again.

Listen to the sound
reverberate in your head.

Feel the vibration in your
throat and face.

Practice for
5 to 10 minutes without
straining the breath.
Sit in silence and notice
the after-effect.

155

Breathing practices can be a powerful resource in grief if focusing on the lungs and the breath feels accessible to you.

When harnessed effectively our breath can calm us down very quickly after or through bouts of crying and allow our emotions to flow through and across the organs of grief through the function of the vagus nerve.

Instead of taking a big inhale to calm down, take a big exhale. Our inhalations increase our heart rate, stimulating our nervous system even more while in an already overly stimulated state.

Long, slow exhales slow our heart rate and invite our bodies to move into rest-and-digest mode.

Counting the breath is a very effective technique that gives the mind something to focus on while bringing the attention to the breath. This can be done lying down or sitting by exhaling for a count of 4, holding the exhale for a count of 4, inhaling for a count of 4, holding on the inhale for a count of 4, eventually increasing the count in each direction as much as feels accessible to you. While walking, steps can be synced up the count, such as 4 steps per inhale, 4 steps retaining the inhale, 4 steps per exhale, 4 steps retaining the exhale.

When using the breath as an anchor or in meditative practices stay sensitive to how your body and mind are responding. Even when we are very practiced at focusing or controlling the breath, there can be instances where new events in our lives can change the way our bodies respond to these practices.

Always choose what supports you best today.

Alternate Nostril Breathing

With eyes open or closed, close off the right nostril gently, without moving the septum.

Inhale through the left nostril.

Close off the left nostril.

Exhale through the right.

Inhale through the right.

Close the right, exhale through the left.

Repeat the cycle for 5 to 10 minutes.

Notice how you feel.

Body Scan

A body scan is a guided meditation, also known as yoga nidra.

A body scan can be done in any position. Feel free to lie down in a comfortable position, take a supported seat, or even stand, perhaps leaning against a wall if that feels best.

Your eyes can be open or closed. You might start with the eyes closed and then feel the urge to open them as the scanning progresses. Honor that instinct.

Get an idea for the practice on the opposite page or listen to the one at TheGriefPractice.com.

Perhaps jot down any points that are important to you if you choose to try any of the meditation practices.

To guide yourself, start by noticing and naming each body part from your feet up to your head. Instead of trying to fix things that you notice, see if you can just observe what is already happening.

It could be something like noticing each toe on the right foot, starting with the big toe, without moving the toes. Feel the heel on the floor, move up to the calf and shin, front and back of the knee, front and back of the thigh, and the right hip.

Switch over to the left foot and repeat the process on the left side. When you get to the left hip, bring your attention to the low belly, perhaps even the abdominal and pelvic organs, and the low back. Continue moving up to the mid-back, upper back and upper chest. Notice the left and right shoulders, front and back, the neck and throat, the back of the head, perhaps even sense the skull inside your head.

Move over to the face. Become aware of each eye and how they rest in the eye sockets. Sense the muscles of the jaw and the lips. Feel the tongue resting inside the mouth. Notice the upper palate and the lower palate, the upper teeth and the lower teeth, the left inner cheek and the right outer cheek.

Become aware of your entire left side and the boundary between your skin and the air. Try this on your right side.

Become aware of your breath. See if you can sense where the breath starts from on the inhale and where it originates on the exhale.
Notice the pauses in between the breath.

Begin to move slowly.

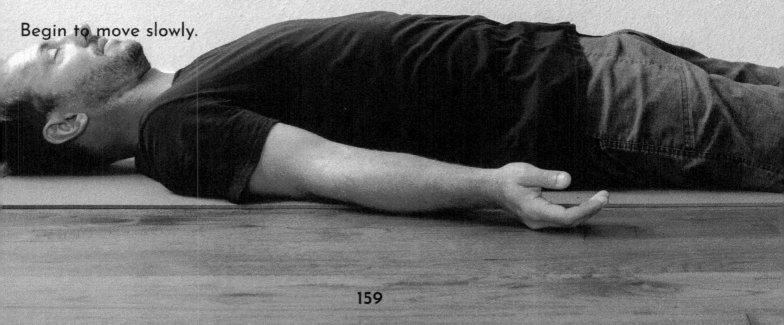

Putting It All Together

Begin in a place and space that feels safe and comfortable to you.

To start, choose an anchor. Write it down if you like. Spend a few minutes connecting with your anchor and settling into your body, just as it is right now. Meet yourself exactly where you are today.

Next, decide if mapping your grief would be helpful today. If you decide yes, scan your body for physical sensations that accompany your grief today and places in the body that feel spacious, grounded, or safe. Notate or draw it if you like so you have something to consider the next time you check in with your grief.

Choose a shape or multiple shapes from the supported or active categories that resonate with your body and energy today.

In a supported practice, once in your shape of choice, pulse your attention between the physical sensations in your body and the places that feel spacious and safe.

When moving through shapes in a more active practice, keep returning to your anchor of choice as you explore the physical sensations in your body.

Adjust your degree of pulsing according to how comfortable and safe you feel exploring your body today.

Acknowledge wherever and however you are today.

Honor the incredible job your body and mind are doing to keep you functioning and healing at their own pace.

We are not changing what happened.
We are changing the way it lives in us.

—Elena Brower

Use this page and the following pages to arrange your practice, keep track of your favorite sequences or shapes, and journal any insights or questions that arise in your practice.

My Practice

anchors

movement

breath

energy

tears

community

shapes

sensation

flow

emotion

explore

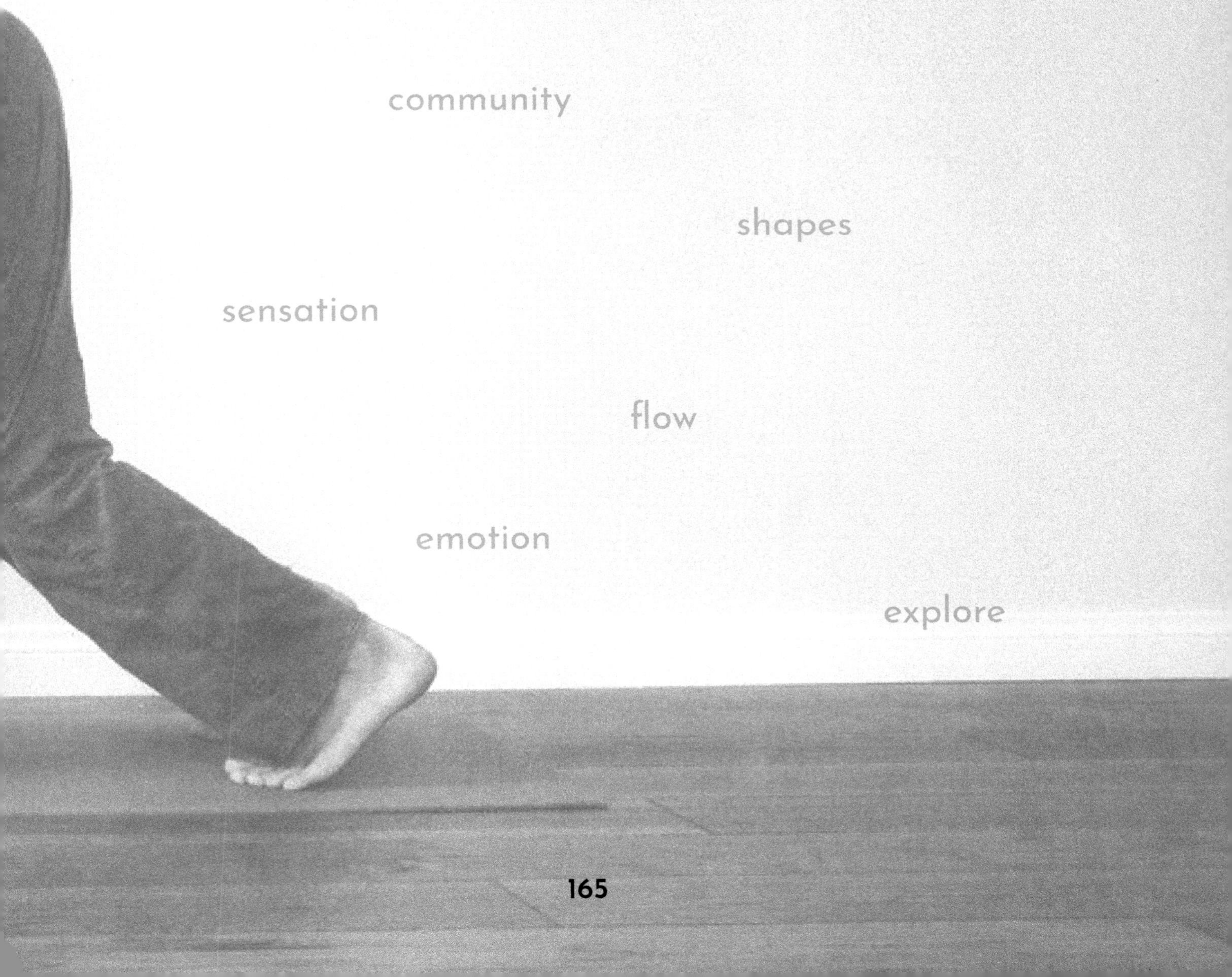

This is where I start.

This is what feels safe.

This is where I explore.

This is what I find.

This is my prayer, gratitude, or intention.

This is how I support my heart.

This is how I remember my love.

This is how I honor my grief.

This is how I return home to me.

Onward, courageous heart

References

1. Childre, D. L., Martin, H., & Beech, D. (2000) p. 137. *The HeartMath solution*. San Francisco, CA: HarperSanFrancisco.

2. Fredrickson, B. (2013) p. 187. *Love 2.0: How our supreme emotion affects everything we feel, think, do, and become*. New York: Hudson Street Press.

3. Porges, S. W. (2017) p. 47. *The pocket guide to polyvagal theory: The transformative power of feeling safe*. New York, NY: W.W Norton & Company.

4. Pert, C. B. (2003) p. 188. *Molecules of Emotion: The Science Behind Mind-Body Medicine*. New York, NY: Scribner.

5. Pert, C. B. (2003) p. 193. *Molecules of Emotion: The Science Behind Mind-Body Medicine*. New York, NY: Scribner.

6. Porges, S. W. (2017) p. 136. *The pocket guide to polyvagal theory: The transformative power of feeling safe*. New York, NY: W.W Norton & Company.

7. Kaptchuk, T. J. (2008) p. 158. *The web that has no weaver: Understanding Chinese medicine*. New York: McGraw-Hill.

8. Van Der Kolk, B. (2015) p. 269. *The body keeps the score: Mind, brain and body in the transformation of trauma*. London: Penguin Books.

9. Childre, D. L., Martin, H., & Beech, D. (2000) p. 37. *The HeartMath solution*. San Francisco, CA: HarperSanFrancisco.

10. Childre, D. L., Martin, H., & Beech, D. (2000) p. 189. *The HeartMath solution*. San Francisco, CA: HarperSanFrancisco.

11. Childre, D. L., Martin, H., & Beech, D. (2000) p. 189. *The HeartMath solution*. San Francisco, CA: HarperSanFrancisco.

12. Childre, D. L., Martin, H., & Beech, D. (2000) p. 33. *The HeartMath solution*. San Francisco, CA: HarperSanFrancisco.

13. Fredrickson, B. (2013) p. 69. *Love 2.0: How our supreme emotion affects everything we feel, think, do, and become*. New York: Hudson Street Press.

14. Is Depression in Old Age Fatal Only When People Feel Lonely? (n.d.). Retrieved from https://ajp.psychiatryonline.org/doi/10.1176/appi.ajp.162.1.178

15. Fredrickson, B. (2013) p. 103. *Love 2.0: How our supreme emotion affects everything we feel, think, do, and become*. New York: Hudson Street Press.

16. Childre, D. L., Martin, H., & Beech, D. (2000) p. 203. *The HeartMath solution.* San Francisco, CA: HarperSanFrancisco.

17. Porges, S. W. (2017) p. 158. *The pocket guide to polyvagal theory: The transformative power of feeling safe.* New York, NY: W.W Norton & Company.

18. Childre, D. L., Martin, H., & Beech, D. (2000) p. 189. *The HeartMath solution.* San Francisco, CA: HarperSanFrancisco.

19. Pert, C. B. (2003) p. 188. *Molecules of Emotion: The Science Behind Mind-Body Medicine.* New York, NY: Scribner.

20. Levine, P. A., & Frederick, A. (1997) p. 67. *Waking the tiger: Healing trauma: The innate capacity to transform overwhelming experiences.* Berkeley, CA: North Atlantic Books.

21. Kalyani, B. G., Venkatasubramanian, G., Arasappa, R., Rao, N. P., Kalmady, S. V., Behere, R. V., . . . Gangadhar, B. N. (2011, March 21). Neurohemodynamic correlates of 'OM' chanting: A pilot functional magnetic resonance imaging study. Retrieved September 17, 2018, from https://www.ncbi.nlm.nih.gov/pmc/articles/PMC3099099/

22. Porges, S. W. (2017) p. 25. *The pocket guide to polyvagal theory: The transformative power of feeling safe.* New York, NY: W.W Norton & Company.

23. Gračanin, Asmir, Bylsma, M., L., & M., J. J. (2014, May 07). Is crying a self-soothing behavior? Retrieved from https://www.frontiersin.org/articles/10.3389/fpsyg.2014.00502/full

24. Berceli, D. (2015) p. 56. *Shake it off naturally: Reduce stress, anxiety, and tension with (Tre).* United States: CreateSpace.

25. Craving love? Enduring grief activates brain's reward center. (2008, May 10). Retrieved from https://www.sciencedirect.com/science/article/pii/S1053811908006101

26. Siegel, D. J., & Bryson, T. P. (2016) p. 205. *No-drama discipline: The whole-brain way to calm the chaos and nurture your child's developing mind.* New York: Bantam Books.

27. Van Der Kolk, B. (2015) p. 63. *The body keeps the score: Mind, brain and body in the transformation of trauma.* London: Penguin Books.

28. Van Der Kolk, B. (2015) p. 286. *The body keeps the score: Mind, brain and body in the transformation of trauma.* London: Penguin Books.

29. Werntz, D. A., Bickford, R. G., Bloom, F. E., & Shannahoff-Khalsa, D. S. (1983, February). Alternating cerebral hemispheric activity and the lateralization of autonomic nervous function. Retrieved September 24, 2017, from https://www.ncbi.nlm.nih.gov/pubmed/6874437

30. Pert, C. B. (2003) p. 272. *Molecules of Emotion: The Science Behind Mind-Body Medicine*. New York, NY: Scribner.

31. Treleaven, D. A. (2018) p. 37. *Trauma-sensitive mindfulness: Practices for safe and transformative healing*. New York: W.W Norton & Company.

32. Treleaven, D. A. (2018) p. 123. *Trauma-sensitive mindfulness: Practices for safe and transformative healing*. New York: W.W Norton & Company.

33. Van Der Kolk, B. (2015) p. 247. *The body keeps the score: Mind, brain and body in the transformation of trauma*. London: Penguin Books.

34. Brogaard, K., Stryger, H. P., Kjaer, M., Aagaard, P., & Magnusson, S. P. (2006, November 01). Passive knee joint range of motion is unrelated to the mechanical properties of the patellar tendon. Retrieved from https://onlinelibrary.wiley.com/doi/abs/10.1111/j.1600-0838.2006.00591.x

35. Porges, S. W. (2017) p. 101. *The pocket guide to polyvagal theory: The transformative power of feeling safe*. New York, NY: W.W Norton & Company.

36. Porges, S. W. (2017) p. 68. *The pocket guide to polyvagal theory: The transformative power of feeling safe*. New York, NY: W.W Norton & Company.

37. Marian E Papp, Petra Lindfors, Niklas Storck, & Wändell. (2013, February 11). Increased heart rate variability but no effect on blood pressure from 8 weeks of hatha yoga – a pilot study. Retrieved from https://bmcresnotes.biomedcentral.com/articles/10.1186/1756-0500-6-59

38. Marks-Tarlow, T., Solomon, M., & Siegel, D. J. (2018) p. 94. *Play and creativity in psychotherapy*. New York: W.W Norton & Company.

39. Nagamatsu, L. S. (2012, April 23). Resistance Training Promotes Cognitive and Functional Brain Plasticity in Seniors With Probable Mild Cognitive Impairment. Retrieved from https://jamanetwork.com/journals/jamainternalmedicine/fullarticle/1135414

40. Treleaven, D. A. (2018) pp. 127-149. *Trauma-sensitive mindfulness: Practices for safe and transformative healing*. New York: W.W Norton & Company.

41. Van Der Kolk, B. (2015) p. 286. *The body keeps the score: Mind, brain and body in the transformation of trauma.* London: Penguin Books.

Photo Credits

Cover, Pages 15, 83, 86, 89: Jacqueline T. Washle

Pages 90, 92, 94, 96: Marissa Quinn. www.marissaquinn-art.com

Pages 105, 111, 118-161, 178-181: Stacey Winters. www.staceywinters.com

Page 112: Jillian Danenhauer

Appendix

Support the belly, chest and head with a bolster or pillow, 5 minutes.

Support the length of the spine, from sacrum to neck, with a folded blanket or towel, 5 minutes.

Twist over a bolster or pillow, 5 minutes each side.

Support the legs with a wall, 5 minutes.

Support the sacrum with a book or block, 5 minutes.

Diaphragm release, 3-5 minutes.

Final resting shape, on the side, belly or back, 5 minutes.

Sample Active Sequence 11

Feel your feet on the ground.

Press each knuckle into the earth.

Keep awareness in the back leg and foot.

Pulse the back knee up and down a few times.

Initiate the twist from the ribs.

Simultaneously press down through the pelvis and lift up with the back.

Play with inhaling into the side ribs, as if you had gills.

Notice the sensation in the toes on the extended leg.

Breathe into the left lung.

Allow for wobbling as you find your balance.

Notice where you feel contracted and where you feel spacious.

Pulse your attention between the breath and the sounds you hear.

After this shape find a downward facing dog, come to standing, and repeat the poses from the beginning on the left leg before continuing on.

Where do you feel the breath on the inhale?

Notice the texture of the mat under your fingertips.

Try to lengthen out each exhale a little longer than the one before.

What does it feel like to be contracted?

What feels good in this shape? Or less bad?

Hug knees into chest before finding a resting shape. Notice the sounds you can hear as your body rests.

Gratitudes

This book was made possible by real humans lending their time, talents, hearts, emotional and financial support.

This is my village:

My Indiegogo family, near and far, whose trust and financial support helped breathe life into this book.

The 20 courageous hearts who trusted me to share their unedited hearts with the world through stories and photos.

My heart sister, Jacqueline Washle, for sharing her drawing talents that created the cover art for the book, as well as pages 15, 83, 86, and 89.

Dear local artist, Marissa Quinn, whose intuition and insight was able to bring my ideas of merging anatomy and spirit to life on pages 90, 92, 94, and 96.

Fellow local yoga teacher, Luke Wientzen, who graciously collaborated on the yoga photos included in the book.

My sister, Nicole Timofeyeva, for her unwavering support of my heart and for her talent, skill, and vision in creating the companion website TheGriefPractice.com.

Local mandala creatrix, Nadia Quiros Horvath, who lovingly guided me through making the mandala for this book featured on page 77.

Family friend and videographer, Jeff Trujillo, who generously created the Indiegogo video for this project.

Local photographer, Stacey Winters, for making the photoshoot for the book feel effortless and fun and for her eye for detail. (Photos on pages 105, 111, 118-161, 178-181)

My husband, Ted, for holding my heart and my hand from start to finish.

My son, whose daily laughter, love, and deep soul inspired me to complete this book.

My name is Monique Minahan. I am a yoga teacher in Carlsbad, California, where I live with my now-husband, son, and little white dog.

I have been motivated to give a voice to grief and shift the stigma around grief ever since my husband Nathan died in 2002, when I was 25 years old.

I wanted to create the kind of intimate and beautiful book I wish I had found in the depths of my grief.

I hope this book supports your heart when you need it the most.

www.moniqueminahan.com
www.thegriefpractice.com

CPSIA information can be obtained
at www.ICGtesting.com
Printed in the USA
BVHW022334200219
540583BV00002B/1/P